Math **Diagnosis** and **Intervention** System
Diagnostic Tests Part 2
Grades 4–6: Booklets F–J

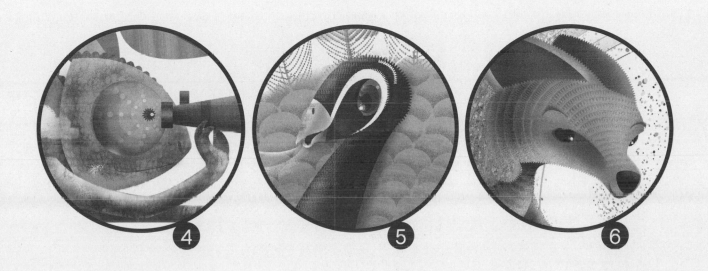

Scott Foresman·Addison Wesley

enVisionMATH™

ISBN-13: 978-0-328-31127-9
ISBN-10: 0-328-31127-8

15 V069 12 11

enVisionMATH is trademarked in the U.S. and/or foreign countries of Pearson Education, Inc. or its affiliate(s).

Editorial Offices: Glenview, Illinois • Parsippany, New Jersey • New York, New York
Sales Offices: Boston, Massachusetts • Duluth, Georgia • Glenview, Illinois
Coppell, Texas • Sacramento, California • Chandler, Arizona

Contents

Diagnostic Tests and Answer Keys

Numeration, Patterns, and Relationships

Read each question. Then mark your answer on the sheet.

1. **Which is the number in expanded form?**

   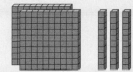

   A 2,000 + 600 + 30

   B 200 + 60 + 3

   C 300 + 60 + 3

   D 600 + 20 + 3

2. **Which is another way to write 6,200?**

   A 62 ones

   B 62 tens

   C 62 hundreds

   D 62 thousands

3. **What is the value of the 7 in 7,045?**

   A Seven

   B Seventy

   C Seven hundred

   D Seven thousand

4. **Which is the standard form?**

   20,000 + 500 + 70 + 9

   A 2,579   **C** 25,079

   B 20,579   **D** 25,709

5. **Which set of numbers is in order from least to greatest?**

   A 452, 392, 425, 375

   B 375, 425, 392, 452

   C 375, 392, 452, 425

   D 375, 392, 425, 452

6. **Which statement is true?**

   A 4,483 > 3,987

   B 653 = 6,053

   C 4,466 < 4,387

   D 2,991 > 3,012

7. **What is 2,817 rounded to the nearest thousand?**

   A 2,000

   B 2,800

   C 2,900

   D 3,000

8. **The boundary between Alaska and Canada is 1,538 miles. What is 1,538 rounded to the nearest hundred?**

   A 1,000

   B 1,500

   C 1,600

   D 2,000

Numeration, Patterns, and Relationships (continued)

Read each question. Then mark your answer on the sheet.

9. Find the rule.

In	Out
2	6
3	9
5	15
7	21

A Add 4.

B Divide by 3.

C Multiply by 3.

D Multiply by 4.

10. Lee made 7 birdhouses each day. How many birdhouses did he complete after 4 days?

Day	1	2	3	4
Birdhouses	7	14	21	?

A 42 birdhouses

B 32 birdhouses

C 36 birdhouses

D 28 birdhouses

11. The first shape shown has 1 row of squares, the second shape has 2 rows, and the third shape has 3 rows.

If the pattern continues, how many squares are in a shape with 5 rows?

Number of Rows	1	2	3	4	5
Number of Squares	3	5	7	?	?

A 8

B 9

C 10

D 11

12. What are the next two shapes in the pattern?

A ⬡ ⬡

B △ ⬡

C ⬡ △

D △ △

Numeration, Patterns, and Relationships (continued)

Read each question. Then mark your answer on the sheet.

---

13. **Find the missing number in the pattern.**

    67, 63, 59, 55, _____

    A 59

    B 61

    C 51

    D 53

---

14. **Which ordered pair names point G?**

    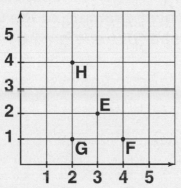

    A (2, 1)

    B (2, 4)

    C (3, 2)

    D (4, 1)

15. **Which numerical expression matches the situation?**

    Mr. Ramirez had 45 pencils at the beginning of the year. The class used 44 pencils.

    A 45 + 44

    B 44 − 45

    C 45 − 44

    D 45 ÷ 44

---

16. **Compare. Use <, >, =, or +.**

    20 + 7 ▧ 34 − 5

    A <

    B >

    C =

    D +

---

17. **Find the missing number.**

    25 − ▧ = 10

    A 9

    B 10

    C 15

    D 20

Operations with Whole Numbers

Read each question. Then mark your answer on the sheet.

---

18. Which is the same as 6 + 5 + 3?

A 6 + 3 + 3

B 4 + 5 + 3

C 5 + 3 + 7

D 3 + 6 + 5

---

19.   50
        − 32

A 12

B 18

C 22

D 28

---

20. Thomas is subtracting 73 − 19 by using compensation. Which of the following could he use?

A Think: 73 − 20 = 53
           53 − 1 = 52
    so, 73 − 19 = 52

B Think: 73 − 20 = 53
           53 + 1 = 54
    so, 73 − 19 = 54

C Think: 75 − 20 = 55
           55 − 2 = 53
    so, 73 − 19 = 53

D Think: 75 − 20 = 55
    so, 73 − 19 = 55

---

21. To add 54 + 20 on a hundred chart, start at 54 and then move which way?

A Right 2 spaces

B Left 2 spaces

C Up 2 rows

D Down 2 rows

---

22. A farm has 296 apple trees and 114 orange trees. Which is the best estimate of the total number of trees on the farm?

A 300 + 200 = 500

B 300 + 100 = 400

C 200 + 200 = 400

D 300 + 0 = 300

---

23.   567
        154
      + 332

A 953   C 1,053

B 1,043   D 1,153

---

24. A $795 bike costs about how much more than a $314 bike?

A $200

B $300

C $500

D $600

Operations with Whole Numbers (continued)

Read each question. Then mark your answer on the sheet.

---

25. 726
    − 143

  A 483

  B 503

  C 523

  D 583

---

26. $7.19
    + $1.86

  A $9.05

  B $8.95

  C $8.05

  D $6.73

---

27. **Which is the same as 3 × 5?**

  A 5 + 5 + 5 + 5

  B 3 + 5

  C 3 + 3 + 3

  D 5 + 5 + 5

---

28. **Holly sold 8 magazines. Her friend sold 10 times as many magazines as Holly. How many magazines did Holly's friend sell?**

  A 18 magazines

  B 80 magazines

  C 88 magazines

  D 96 magazines

---

29. **Find the missing number.**

  $$7 \times \blacksquare = 0$$

  A 0   C 2

  B 1   D 3

---

30. 11 × 8 =

  A 88   C 77

  B 80   D 19

---

31. **Which number sentences describe the array?**

  A 3 × 3 = 9 and 9 ÷ 3 = 3

  B 3 × 4 = 12 and 12 ÷ 3 = 4

  C 3 × 6 = 18 and 18 ÷ 3 = 6

  D 3 × 5 = 15 and 15 ÷ 3 = 5

---

32. **Hiroshi has 4 rows of pictures. There are 9 pictures in each row. How many pictures does Hiroshi have in all?**

  A 36 pictures

  B 32 pictures

  C 27 pictures

  D 13 pictures

Operations with Whole Numbers (continued)

Read each question. Then mark your answer on the sheet.

---

33. Sean divides $54 equally among 6 people. How much money did each person get?

A $7   C $9

B $8   D $10

---

34. $4\overline{)4}$

A 0   C 4

B 1   D 16

---

35. Paula has 18 dolls in her collection. She puts them into 4 equal groups. How many dolls are left?

A 4 dolls   C 2 dolls

B 3 dolls   D 1 doll

---

36. Which shows 2 × 35?

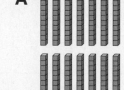
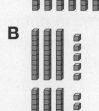
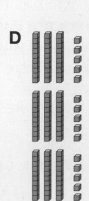

---

37. At the gift shop, each beach towel costs $18. If you bought 4 beach towels, about how much did you spend?

A About $40

B About $60

C About $80

D About $100

---

38. Karen bought 3 new shirts for $17 each. How much money did she spend?

A $41

B $20

C $50

D $51

---

39. There are 90 students in 3 classes. How many students are in each class if each class is the same size?

A 270 students

B 30 students

C 27 students

D 25 students

---

40. $7\overline{)91}$

A 15   C 13

B 14   D 12

Fractions, Decimals, and Percents

Read each question. Then mark your answer on the sheet.

---

41. Which shape is $\frac{7}{8}$ shaded?

A

B

C

D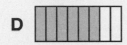

---

42. How much is left? Estimate.

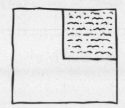

A About $\frac{1}{3}$

B About $\frac{1}{2}$

C About $\frac{1}{4}$

D About $\frac{2}{4}$

---

43. Write the missing fractions for the number line.

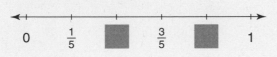

A $\frac{2}{5}, \frac{5}{5}$ **C** $\frac{2}{5}, \frac{4}{5}$

B $\frac{3}{5}, \frac{4}{5}$ **D** $\frac{1}{5}, \frac{2}{5}$

---

44. Which fraction is equivalent to $\frac{1}{2}$?

A $\frac{2}{6}$ **C** $\frac{4}{8}$

B $\frac{4}{9}$ **D** $\frac{3}{5}$

---

45. Use the fraction models. Which is true?

A $\frac{3}{4} < \frac{2}{4}$ **C** $\frac{3}{4} > \frac{2}{4}$

B $\frac{3}{4} = \frac{2}{4}$ **D** $\frac{1}{4} > \frac{2}{4}$

---

46. Katrina has these coins. What is the total value of her coins?

A $0.52

B $0.57

C $0.62

D $0.67

Fractions, Decimals, and Percents (continued)

Read each question. Then mark your answer on the sheet.

47. **Jon's lunch costs $4.83. He pays with a $5 bill. Which coins are his change?**

 A 2 dimes, 2 pennies

 B 2 dimes, 1 penny

 C 1 dime, 2 pennies

 D 1 dime, 7 pennies

48. **In the shape below, $\frac{7}{10}$ is shaded. Which decimal equals $\frac{7}{10}$?**

 A 0.8

 B 0.7

 C 0.08

 D 0.07

49. **How do you make $9.45 using only dollars, dimes, and pennies?**

 A 9 dollars, 5 dimes, and 4 pennies

 B 9 dollars, 45 dimes, and 4 pennies

 C 9 dollars, 4 dimes, and 5 pennies

 D 9 dollars, 5 dimes, and 5 pennies

50. **Ayla ate $\frac{6}{10}$ of the grapes and Mandy ate $\frac{1}{10}$ of them. What part of the grapes did they eat in all?**

 A $\frac{7}{10}$

 B $\frac{6}{10}$

 C $\frac{5}{10}$

 D $\frac{4}{10}$

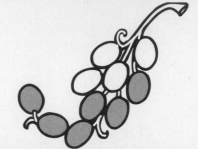

51. **Mario used $\frac{7}{10}$ yard of rope for his project. Sam used $\frac{5}{10}$ yard of rope for his project. How much more rope did Mario use?**

 A $\frac{1}{5}$ yard

 B $\frac{1}{2}$ yard

 C $1\frac{1}{5}$ yards

 D 2 yards

Measurement and Geometry

Read each question. Then mark your answer on the sheet.

---

52. What is the name of this figure?

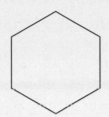

A Rectangle

B Pentagon

C Hexagon

D Octagon

---

53. Which describes the triangle?

A Equilateral

B Right

C Obtuse

D Acute

---

54. Which describes the figure?

A Parallelogram

B Square

C Rectangle

D Rhombus

---

55. How was this figure moved?

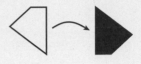

A flip

B slide

C flip then slide

D turn

---

56. Which letter has more than one line of symmetry?

A The letter M

B The letter T

C The letter E

D The letter O

---

57. Which solid figure does *not* have any corners?

A

B

C

D

Measurement and Geometry (continued)

Read each question. Then mark your answer on the sheet.

---

58. What is the length of the piece of yarn to the nearest $\frac{1}{4}$ inch?

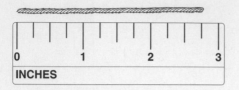

A $2\frac{3}{4}$ inches

B 2 inches

C $2\frac{1}{4}$ inches

D 3 inches

---

59. Which item weighs about 1 kilogram?

A Bicycle

B Ring

C Book

D Postcard

---

60. What is the best estimate for how much the container of milk holds?

A 1 cup

B 1 pint

C 1 quart

D 1 gallon

---

61. Which is the best estimate for the length of a pencil?

A 2 m

B 15 cm

C 1 km

D 2 cm

---

62. Which temperature does the thermometer show?

A 45°C

B 75°F

C 85°C

D 85°F

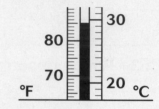

---

63. What time is shown on the clock?

A 8:52

B 8:50

C 7:55

D 7:52

Measurement and Geometry (continued)

Read each question. Then mark your answer on the sheet.

---

64. Practice for the play lasted from 3:45 P.M. to 5:10 P.M. How long did practice last?

  A 1 hour 15 minutes

  B 1 hour 25 minutes

  C 1 hour 35 minutes

  D 2 hours 35 minutes

---

65. Find the perimeter of this shape.

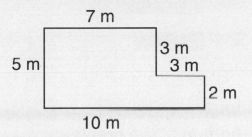

  A 25 meters

  B 27 meters

  C 30 meters

  D 32 meters

---

66. What is the area of the grid?

  A 9 square units

  B 18 square units

  C 20 square units

  D 25 square units

---

67. Which could be the length and width of a rectangle with the same perimeter as the rectangle shown?

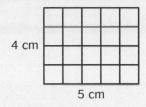

  A 3 cm by 6 cm

  B 3 cm by 5 cm

  C 2 cm by 6 cm

  D 2 cm by 5 cm

---

68. What is the volume of the solid?

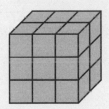

  A 6 cubic units

  B 12 cubic units

  C 15 cubic units

  D 18 cubic units

Data Analysis and Probability

Read each question. Then mark your answer on the sheet.

Use the pictograph to answer Questions 69–71.

Our Favorite Fruit

bananas	🚹🚹🚹🚹
apples	🚹🚹🚹🚹🚹🚹🚹
pears	🚹🚹
oranges	🚹🚹🚹🚹🚹

Key: 🚹 = 2 children

69. How many children chose oranges as their favorite fruit?

A 10   C 5

B 7   D 4

70. How many more children chose apples than oranges?

A 3

B 4

C 9

D 5

71. How many symbols should Caro draw in another row of the graph to show that 6 children chose peaches?

A 3

B 4

C 5

D 6

Mrs. Green divided her class into three reading teams. She created a bar graph to chart the number of books each group read.

Use the graph for Questions 72 and 73.

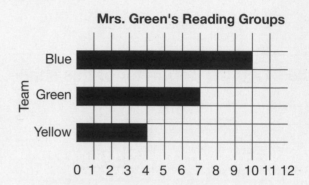

Mrs. Green's Reading Groups

72. What is the best label for the bottom of the graph?

A Number of Books read by Mrs. Green

B Team

C Number of Books Read

D Number of Books read by the Yellow Team

73. How many more books did the Blue Team read than the Yellow Team?

A 3 books

B 6 books

C 10 books

D 14 books

Data Analysis and Probability (continued)

Read each question. Then mark your answer on the sheet.

---

74. Members of the Sky Blue Club wrote their names on cards.

Luisa   Emily   Billy

Hongi   Debby   Tammy

If you choose one of the cards without looking, what is the likelihood that you will get a card with a name that has 5 letters?

A Impossible   **C** Likely

B Unlikely   **D** Certain

---

75. Emeril tossed 5 coins 70 times. The table shows the outcomes.

5 heads	II
4 heads, 1 tail	LHT LHT I
3 heads, 2 tails	LHT LHT III
2 heads, 3 tails	LHT LHT LHT LHT LHT III
1 head, 4 tails	LHT LHT
5 tails	LHT I

To win the game, you must predict the next outcome correctly. Based on the previous results, which should you choose?

A 4 heads, 1 tail

B 3 heads, 2 tails

C 2 heads, 3 tails

D 1 head, 4 tails

---

76. Which outcome is most likely when the spinner below is spun once?

A 1

B 2

C 3

D All

---

77. Roberto kept track of the number of rainy days each week for 12 weeks. His results are shown in the line plot below.

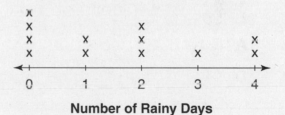

Number of Rainy Days

What is the most likely number of rainy days next week?

A 0 days

B 1 day

C 2 days

D 4 days

Problem Solving

Read each question. Then mark your answer on the sheet.

---

78. Sue places 3 pencils end-to-end on her desk. The first pencil is 7 inches long. The second pencil is 5 inches long. What information do you need to find the total length of the 3 pencils?

  A The length of the first pencil

  B The length of the second pencil

  C The length of the third pencil

  D The length of Sue's desk

---

79. Jack buys 2 notebooks for $4 each. He also buys 3 pens for $2 each. How much does Jack spend in all?

  A $6

  B $8

  C $10

  D $14

---

80. Harry has 30 stamps on 5 pages of his stamp album. There are the same number of stamps on each page. Which number sentence can be used to find how many stamps are on each page?

  A $30 + 5 = 35$

  B $30 - 5 = 25$

  C $5 \times 30 = 150$

  D $30 \div 5 = 6$

---

81. How many different breakfasts can you choose?

Breakfast Choices
Eggs or pancakes
Bacon or sausage

  A 8   **C** 4

  B 6   **D** 2

---

82. The Pizza Place gives 2 free pens with each slice of pizza. John buys 4 slices of pizza. How many free pens does he get?

Slices of pizza	1	2	3	4
Free pens	2	4	?	?

  A 2   **C** 16

  B 4   **D** 8

---

83. Which description is true about the figures shown?

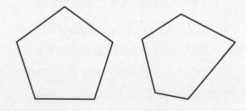

  A Both figures have 5 right angles.

  B Both figures are solid shapes.

  C Both figures have 4 sides.

  D Both figures have 5 sides.

Numeration, Patterns, and Relationships

Read each question. Then mark your answer on the sheet.

---

1. **Which is the number in expanded form?**

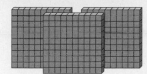

   A 3,000 + 400 + 20

   B 300 + 40 + 20

   C 200 + 40 + 2

   D 300 + 40 + 2

2. **Which is another way to write 7,500?**

   A 75 ones

   B 75 tens

   C 75 hundreds

   D 75 thousands

3. **What is the value of the 6 in 6,502?**

   A Six

   B Sixty

   C Six hundred

   D Six thousand

4. **Which is the standard form?**

   30,000 + 8,000 + 20

   A 382   C 38,020

   B 30,820   D 380,020

5. **Which set of numbers is in order from least to greatest?**

   A 673, 281, 637, 264

   B 264, 637, 281, 673

   C 264, 281, 637, 673

   D 264, 281, 673, 637

6. **Which statement is true?**

   A 3,122 < 2,999

   B 542 = 5,042

   C 6,076 > 8,001

   D 1,363 < 1,403

7. **What is 6,483 rounded to the nearest thousand?**

   A 6,000

   B 6,400

   C 6,500

   D 7,000

8. **The U.S. Constitution contains 4,543 words, including the signatures. What is 4,543 rounded to the nearest hundred?**

   A 4,000

   B 4,500

   C 4,600

   D 5,000

Numeration, Patterns, and Relationships (continued)

Read each question. Then mark your answer on the sheet.

9. Find the rule.

In	Out
2	10
4	20
5	25
7	35

   A Multiply by 8.

   B Multiply by 5.

   C Add 8.

   D Divide by 5.

10. Max needs to water each of his pepper plants with 2 cups of water. How many cups of water will he need for 5 pepper plants?

Pepper plants	1	2	3	4	5
Cups of water	2	4	?	?	?

   A 7 cups

   B 10 cups

   C 12 cups

   D 14 cups

11. The first shape shown has 1 row of squares, the second shape has 2 rows, and the third shape has 3 rows.

If the pattern continues, how many squares are in a shape with 5 rows?

Number of Rows	1	2	3	4	5
Number of Squares	4	6	8	?	?

   A 10

   B 11

   C 12

   D 14

12. What are the next two shapes in the pattern?

   A

   B

   C

   D

Numeration, Patterns, and Relationships (continued)

Read each question. Then mark your answer on the sheet.

13. **Find the missing number in the pattern.**

    55, 49, 43, 37, _____

    A 38

    B 33

    C 31

    D 30

14. **Which ordered pair names point Q?**

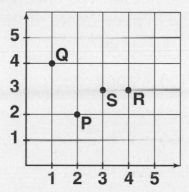

    A (1, 4)

    B (2, 2)

    C (3, 3)

    D (4, 3)

15. **Which numerical expression matches the situation?**

    Twenty children were singing. Then 5 children stopped singing.

    A 20 + 5

    B 20 × 5

    C 20 − 5

    D 5 − 20

16. **Compare. Use <, >, =, or +.**

    17 + 4 ■ 25 − 7

    A <

    B >

    C =

    D +

17. **Find the missing number.**

    14 + ■ = 24

    A 9

    B 10

    C 11

    D 38

Operations with Whole Numbers

Read each question. Then mark your answer on the sheet.

---

18. Which is the same as 7 + 4 + 9?

A 7 + 9 + 5

B 4 + 3 + 9

C 9 + 7 + 4

D 9 + 0 + 7

---

19. 60
      − 24

A 44

B 40

C 36

D 26

---

20. Rachael is adding 49 + 16 by using compensation. Which of the following could she use?

A Think: 50 + 16 = 66
     so, 49 + 16 = 66

B Think: 50 + 16 = 66
         66 + 1 = 67
     so, 49 + 16 = 67

C Think: 50 + 16 = 66
         66 − 1 = 65
     so, 49 + 16 = 65

D Think: 50 + 17 = 67
         67 + 1 = 68
     so, 49 + 16 = 68

---

21. To subtract 75 − 30 on a hundred chart, start at 75 and then move which way?

A Right 3 spaces

B Left 3 spaces

C Up 3 rows

D Down 3 rows

---

22. Bruce scored 106 points. His friend scored 189 points. Which is the best estimate of the total points scored?

A 100 + 200 = 300

B 100 + 100 = 200

C 200 + 200 = 400

D 0 + 200 = 200

---

23.   736
        183
      + 241

A 1,060   C 1,150

B 1,061   D 1,160

---

24. A 907-mile trip is about how much longer than a 485-mile trip?

A 400 miles

B 500 miles

C 600 miles

D 700 miles

Operations with Whole Numbers (continued)

Read each question. Then mark your answer on the sheet.

---

25.   857
     − 368

   A 489

   B 499

   C 511

   D 599

---

26. $5.47
     + $3.84

   A $8.31

   B $9.21

   C $9.31

   D $9.32

---

27. **Which is the same as 4 × 3?**

   A 3 + 3 + 3

   B 4 + 3

   C 3 + 3 + 3 + 3

   D 4 + 4 + 4 + 4

---

28. **Chris has 6 books. His brother has 10 times as many books as Chris. How many books does his brother have?**

   A 16 books

   B 60 books

   C 66 books

   D 106 books

---

29. **Find the missing number.**

   $$8 \times \blacksquare = 0$$

   A 0   **C** 2

   B 1   **D** 3

---

30. **7 × 11 =**

   A 18   **C** 77

   B 70   **D** 84

---

31. **Which number sentences describe the array?**

   A 3 × 3 = 9 and 9 ÷ 3 = 3

   B 3 × 5 = 15 and 15 ÷ 3 = 5

   C 3 × 6 = 18 and 18 ÷ 3 = 6

   D 3 × 8 = 24 and 24 ÷ 3 = 8

---

32. **Elena planted 8 rows of tulips. She put 6 tulips in each row. How many tulips did she plant in all?**

   A 48 tulips

   B 42 tulips

   C 40 tulips

   D 14 tulips

Operations with Whole Numbers (continued)

Read each question. Then mark your answer on the sheet.

---

33. Micah divides $72 equally among 8 people. How much money did each person get?

    A $6

    B $8

    C $9

    D $12

---

34. 9)9

    A 0   **C** 4

    B 1   **D** 16

---

35. Toruo has 36 stamps in his collection. He puts them into 5 equal groups. How many stamps are left over?

    A 7   **C** 2

    B 6   **D** 1

---

36. Which shows 3 × 37?

    A   **C**

    B 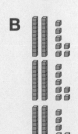   **D**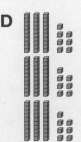

---

37. Video games are on sale for $28 each. If you bought 3 video games, about how much did you spend?

    A About $60

    B About $70

    C About $90

    D About $100

---

38. Lee bought 5 basketballs for $19 each. How much money did he spend?

    A $95

    B $90

    C $54

    D $24

---

39. There are 3 buses to transport 120 students. How many students will ride on each bus if each bus has the same number of students?

    A 20 students

    B 30 students

    C 40 students

    D 60 students

---

40. 5)75

    A 16   **C** 14

    B 15   **D** 12

Fractions, Decimals, and Percents

Read each question. Then mark your answer on the sheet.

---

41. Which shape is $\frac{7}{10}$ shaded?

A

B

C

D

---

42. How much is left? Estimate.

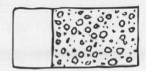

A About $\frac{1}{2}$

B About $\frac{5}{6}$

C About $\frac{3}{4}$

D About $\frac{2}{3}$

---

43. Write the missing fractions for the number line.

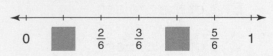

A $\frac{1}{6}, \frac{5}{6}$

B $\frac{2}{6}, \frac{4}{6}$

C $\frac{1}{6}, \frac{4}{6}$

D $\frac{1}{6}, \frac{3}{6}$

---

44. Which fraction is equivalent to $\frac{1}{3}$?

A $\frac{2}{6}$ C $\frac{3}{5}$

B $\frac{2}{5}$ D $\frac{3}{4}$

---

45. Use the fraction models. Which is true?

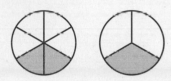

A $\frac{2}{6} > \frac{1}{3}$ C $\frac{2}{6} < \frac{1}{3}$

B $\frac{2}{6} - \frac{1}{3}$ D $\frac{1}{2} < \frac{1}{3}$

---

46. Carlos has these coins. What is the total value of his coins?

A $0.51

B $0.71

C $0.76

D $0.81

Fractions, Decimals, and Percents (continued)

Read each question. Then mark your answer on the sheet.

---

47. Joseppi used a $5 bill to buy a chess set that cost $4.89. Which coins are his change?

    A 2 dimes, 1 penny

    B 1 dime, 1 penny

    C 1 dime

    D 9 pennies

---

48. In the shape below, $\frac{8}{10}$ is shaded. Which decimal equals $\frac{8}{10}$?

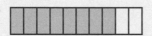

    A 0.08

    B 0.09

    C 0.8

    D 0.9

---

49. How do you make $8.73 using only dollars, dimes, and pennies?

    A 8 dollars, 3 dimes, and 7 pennies

    B 8 dollars, 7 dimes, and 3 pennies

    C 8 dollars, 73 dimes, and 3 pennies

    D 8 dollars, 7 dimes, and 7 pennies

---

50. Tia used $\frac{5}{8}$ of the bananas to make banana bread and $\frac{2}{8}$ of them in a fruit salad. What part of the bananas did she use in all?

    A $\frac{1}{8}$

    B $\frac{3}{8}$

    C $\frac{6}{8}$

    D $\frac{7}{8}$

---

51. Josh finished $\frac{5}{8}$ of his project Monday and $\frac{3}{8}$ on Tuesday. How much more of the project did he finish on Monday than Tuesday?

    A $\frac{1}{4}$ of the project

    B $\frac{3}{8}$ of the project

    C $\frac{1}{2}$ of the project

    D All of the project

Measurement and Geometry

Read each question. Then mark your answer on the sheet.

---

52. What is the name of this figure?

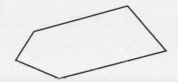

A Octagon

B Pentagon

C Hexagon

D Rectangle

---

53. Which describes the triangle?

A Acute

B Right

C Obtuse

D Equilateral

---

54. Which describes the figure?

A Square

B Rectangle

C Rhombus

D Isosceles

---

55. How was this figure moved?

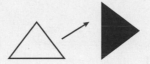

A turn   **C** slide

B flip   **D** flip then slide

---

56. Which of these objects usually has exactly one line of symmetry?

A Butterfly

B Snowflake

C Rock

D Cloud

---

57. Which solid figure does *not* have any corners?

A

B

C

D

Measurement and Geometry (continued)

Read each question. Then mark your answer on the sheet.

---

58. What is the length of the paper clip to the nearest $\frac{1}{4}$ inch?

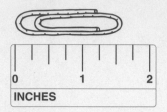

A 1 inch

B $1\frac{1}{2}$ inches

C 2 inches

D $2\frac{1}{4}$ inches

---

59. Which item has a mass of about 1 gram?

A Bowling ball

B Cantaloupe

C Calculator

D Feather

---

60. What is the best estimate for the amount of juice in a juice box?

A 1 cup

B 1 pint

C 1 quart

D 1 gallon

---

61. What is the best estimate for the length of a kitchen table?

A 2 m

B 4 cm

C 6 m

D 1 km

---

62. Which temperature does the thermometer show?

A 70°F

B 82°F

C 29°C

D 39°C

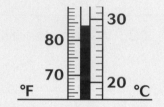

---

63. What time is shown on the clock?

A 8:27

B 8:32

C 8:37

D 9:37

Measurement and Geometry (continued)

Read each question. Then mark your answer on the sheet.

---

64. The concert lasted from 6:45 P.M. to 9:10 P.M. How long did the concert last?

A 3 hours 35 minutes

B 2 hours 35 minutes

C 2 hours 25 minutes

D 2 hours 15 minutes

---

65. Which is the perimeter of this shape?

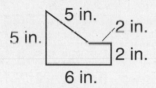

A 11 inches

B 13 inches

C 20 inches

D 30 inches

---

66. What is the area of the rectangle?

A 20 square units

B 24 square units

C 28 square units

D 32 square units

---

67. Which could be the length and width of a rectangle with the same perimeter as the rectangle shown?

A 3 cm by 6 cm

B 3 cm by 4 cm

C 2 cm by 7 cm

D 3 cm by 5 cm

---

68. What is the volume of the solid?

A 12 cubic units

B 18 cubic units

C 27 cubic units

D 30 cubic units

Data Analysis and Probability

Read each question. Then mark your answer on the sheet.

Use the pictograph to answer
Questions 69–71.

Number of Trees in the National Park

Oak	🌳🌳🌳
Pine	🌳🌳🌳🌳🌳🌳
Ash	🌳🌳🌳🌳🌳
Maple	🌳🌳🌳🌳🌳🌳🌳

Key: 🌳 = 5 trees

69. **How many ash trees are in the park?**

A 15   **C** 25

B 20   **D** 35

70. **How many more maple trees are there than pine trees?**

A 5

B 10

C 20

D 25

71. **How many symbols should Ronaldo draw in another row of the graph to show that there are 20 walnut trees in the park?**

A 20

B 10

C 5

D 4

Greta's class is voting on themes for class parties. She created the graph below to show the votes each type of party got. Use the graph for Questions 72 and 73.

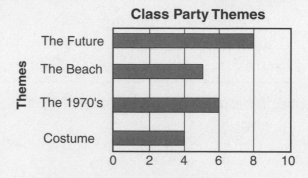

Class Party Themes

72. **What is the best label for the bottom of the graph?**

A Number Voting for a Costume Party

B Themes

C Number of Parties

D Number of Votes

73. **How many more students voted for a future party than voted for a beach party?**

A 1

B 2

C 3

D 4

26

Data Analysis and Probability (continued)

Read each question. Then mark your answer on the sheet.

---

74. Members of the Sky Blue Club wrote their names on cards.

Wendy Emily Billy

Hongi Debby Tammy

If you choose one card without looking, what is the likelihood that you will get a card with a name that ends in y?

A Impossible

B Unlikely

C Likely

D Certain

---

75. Horatio tossed 3 two-colored counters 100 times. The table shows the outcomes.

3 red	JHT JHT IIII
2 red, 1 yellow	JHT JHT JHT JHT JHT JHT JHT JHT JHT IIII
1 red, 2 yellow	JHT JHT JHT JHT JHT II
3 yellow	JHT JHT

To win the game, you must predict the next outcome correctly. Based on the previous results, which should you choose?

A 3 red

B 2 red, 1 yellow

C 1 red, 2 yellow

D 3 yellow

---

76. Which outcome is most likely when the spinner below is spun once?

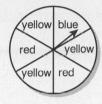

A Blue

B Red

C Yellow

D All

---

77. Roberto kept track of the number of rainy days each week for 12 weeks. His results are shown in the line plot below.

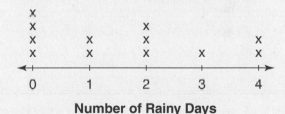

Number of Rainy Days

What is the least likely number of rainy days next week?

A 0 days

B 1 day

C 2 days

D 3 days

Problem Solving

Read each question. Then mark your answer on the sheet.

---

78. Rashid draws 3 rectangles end-to-end on a piece of paper. The first rectangle is 4 inches long. The third rectangle is 2 inches long. What information do you need to find the total length of the 3 rectangles?

  A The length of the first rectangle

  B The length of the second rectangle

  C The length of the third rectangle

  D The length of the piece of paper

---

79. Shasta buys 3 books for $5 each. She also buys 2 newspapers for $1 each. How much does Shasta spend in all?

  A $5   **C** $15

  B $6   **D** $17

---

80. Celina has 48 photos on 8 pages of her photo album. There are the same number of photos on each page. Which number sentence can be used to find how many photos are on each page?

  A $48 + 8 = 56$

  B $48 - 8 = 40$

  C $8 \times 48 = 384$

  D $48 \div 8 = 6$

---

81. How many different kinds of soccer uniforms can you choose?

Soccer Uniforms
• Red or white top
• Black or brown shorts

  A 8   **C** 4

  B 6   **D** 2

---

82. The Supply Store gives 3 free pencils with each notebook you buy. Mia buys 4 notebooks. How many free pencils does she get?

Notebooks	1	2	3	4
Free pencils	3	6	?	?

  A 3   **C** 10

  B 8   **D** 12

---

83. Which statement does NOT belong in the description for the figures shown?

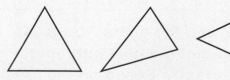

  A All are acute triangles.

  B No angles are obtuse.

  C All sides are different lengths.

  D All figures are polygons.

Answer Sheet

Mark the space that corresponds to the correct answer.   Form A ___   Form B ___

Numeration, Patterns, and Relationships

1. Ⓐ Ⓑ Ⓒ Ⓓ
2. Ⓐ Ⓑ Ⓒ Ⓓ
3. Ⓐ Ⓑ Ⓒ Ⓓ
4. Ⓐ Ⓑ Ⓒ Ⓓ
5. Ⓐ Ⓑ Ⓒ Ⓓ
6. Ⓐ Ⓑ Ⓒ Ⓓ
7. Ⓐ Ⓑ Ⓒ Ⓓ
8. Ⓐ Ⓑ Ⓒ Ⓓ
9. Ⓐ Ⓑ Ⓒ Ⓓ
10. Ⓐ Ⓑ Ⓒ Ⓓ
11. Ⓐ Ⓑ Ⓒ Ⓓ
12. Ⓐ Ⓑ Ⓒ Ⓓ
13. Ⓐ Ⓑ Ⓒ Ⓓ
14. Ⓐ Ⓑ Ⓒ Ⓓ
15. Ⓐ Ⓑ Ⓒ Ⓓ
16. Ⓐ Ⓑ Ⓒ Ⓓ
17. Ⓐ Ⓑ Ⓒ Ⓓ

Operations with Whole Numbers

18. Ⓐ Ⓑ Ⓒ Ⓓ
19. Ⓐ Ⓑ Ⓒ Ⓓ
20. Ⓐ Ⓑ Ⓒ Ⓓ
21. Ⓐ Ⓑ Ⓒ Ⓓ

22. Ⓐ Ⓑ Ⓒ Ⓓ
23. Ⓐ Ⓑ Ⓒ Ⓓ
24. Ⓐ Ⓑ Ⓒ Ⓓ
25. Ⓐ Ⓑ Ⓒ Ⓓ
26. Ⓐ Ⓑ Ⓒ Ⓓ
27. Ⓐ Ⓑ Ⓒ Ⓓ
28. Ⓐ Ⓑ Ⓒ Ⓓ
29. Ⓐ Ⓑ Ⓒ Ⓓ
30. Ⓐ Ⓑ Ⓒ Ⓓ
31. Ⓐ Ⓑ Ⓒ Ⓓ
32. Ⓐ Ⓑ Ⓒ Ⓓ
33. Ⓐ Ⓑ Ⓒ Ⓓ
34. Ⓐ Ⓑ Ⓒ Ⓓ
35. Ⓐ Ⓑ Ⓒ Ⓓ
36. Ⓐ Ⓑ Ⓒ Ⓓ
37. Ⓐ Ⓑ Ⓒ Ⓓ
38. Ⓐ Ⓑ Ⓒ Ⓓ
39. Ⓐ Ⓑ Ⓒ Ⓓ
40. Ⓐ Ⓑ Ⓒ Ⓓ

Fractions, Decimals, and Percents

41. Ⓐ Ⓑ Ⓒ Ⓓ
42. Ⓐ Ⓑ Ⓒ Ⓓ
43. Ⓐ Ⓑ Ⓒ Ⓓ
44. Ⓐ Ⓑ Ⓒ Ⓓ

Answer Sheet (continued)

Mark the space that corresponds to the correct answer.   Form A ____   Form B ____

45. Ⓐ Ⓑ Ⓒ Ⓓ

46. Ⓐ Ⓑ Ⓒ Ⓓ

47. Ⓐ Ⓑ Ⓒ Ⓓ

48. Ⓐ Ⓑ Ⓒ Ⓓ

49. Ⓐ Ⓑ Ⓒ Ⓓ

50. Ⓐ Ⓑ Ⓒ Ⓓ

51. Ⓐ Ⓑ Ⓒ Ⓓ

Measurement and Geometry

52. Ⓐ Ⓑ Ⓒ Ⓓ

53. Ⓐ Ⓑ Ⓒ Ⓓ

54. Ⓐ Ⓑ Ⓒ Ⓓ

55. Ⓐ Ⓑ Ⓒ Ⓓ

56. Ⓐ Ⓑ Ⓒ Ⓓ

57. Ⓐ Ⓑ Ⓒ Ⓓ

58. Ⓐ Ⓑ Ⓒ Ⓓ

59. Ⓐ Ⓑ Ⓒ Ⓓ

60. Ⓐ Ⓑ Ⓒ Ⓓ

61. Ⓐ Ⓑ Ⓒ Ⓓ

62. Ⓐ Ⓑ Ⓒ Ⓓ

63. Ⓐ Ⓑ Ⓒ Ⓓ

64. Ⓐ Ⓑ Ⓒ Ⓓ

65. Ⓐ Ⓑ Ⓒ Ⓓ

66. Ⓐ Ⓑ Ⓒ Ⓓ

67. Ⓐ Ⓑ Ⓒ Ⓓ

68. Ⓐ Ⓑ Ⓒ Ⓓ

Data Analysis and Probability

69. Ⓐ Ⓑ Ⓒ Ⓓ

70. Ⓐ Ⓑ Ⓒ Ⓓ

71. Ⓐ Ⓑ Ⓒ Ⓓ

72. Ⓐ Ⓑ Ⓒ Ⓓ

73. Ⓐ Ⓑ Ⓒ Ⓓ

74. Ⓐ Ⓑ Ⓒ Ⓓ

75. Ⓐ Ⓑ Ⓒ Ⓓ

76. Ⓐ Ⓑ Ⓒ Ⓓ

77. Ⓐ Ⓑ Ⓒ Ⓓ

Problem Solving

78. Ⓐ Ⓑ Ⓒ Ⓓ

79. Ⓐ Ⓑ Ⓒ Ⓓ

80. Ⓐ Ⓑ Ⓒ Ⓓ

81. Ⓐ Ⓑ Ⓒ Ⓓ

82. Ⓐ Ⓑ Ⓒ Ⓓ

83. Ⓐ Ⓑ Ⓒ Ⓓ

Answer Key

Mark the space that corresponds to the correct answer.   Form A ✔ Form B ___

Numeration, Patterns, and Relationships

1. Ⓐ **Ⓑ** Ⓒ Ⓓ
2. Ⓐ Ⓑ **Ⓒ** Ⓓ
3. Ⓐ Ⓑ Ⓒ **Ⓓ**
4. Ⓐ **Ⓑ** Ⓒ Ⓓ
5. Ⓐ Ⓑ Ⓒ **Ⓓ**
6. **Ⓐ** Ⓑ Ⓒ Ⓓ
7. Ⓐ Ⓑ Ⓒ **Ⓓ**
8. Ⓐ **Ⓑ** Ⓒ Ⓓ
9. Ⓐ Ⓑ **Ⓒ** Ⓓ
10. Ⓐ Ⓑ Ⓒ **Ⓓ**
11. Ⓐ Ⓑ Ⓒ **Ⓓ**
12. Ⓐ Ⓑ **Ⓒ** Ⓓ
13. Ⓐ Ⓑ **Ⓒ** Ⓓ
14. **Ⓐ** Ⓑ Ⓒ Ⓓ
15. Ⓐ Ⓑ **Ⓒ** Ⓓ
16. **Ⓐ** Ⓑ Ⓒ Ⓓ
17. Ⓐ Ⓑ **Ⓒ** Ⓓ

Operations with Whole Numbers

18. Ⓐ Ⓑ Ⓒ **Ⓓ**
19. Ⓐ **Ⓑ** Ⓒ Ⓓ
20. Ⓐ **Ⓑ** Ⓒ Ⓓ
21. Ⓐ Ⓑ Ⓒ **Ⓓ**

22. Ⓐ **Ⓑ** Ⓒ Ⓓ
23. Ⓐ Ⓑ **Ⓒ** Ⓓ
24. Ⓐ Ⓑ **Ⓒ** Ⓓ
25. Ⓐ Ⓑ Ⓒ **Ⓓ**
26. **Ⓐ** Ⓑ Ⓒ Ⓓ
27. Ⓐ Ⓑ Ⓒ **Ⓓ**
28. Ⓐ **Ⓑ** Ⓒ Ⓓ
29. **Ⓐ** Ⓑ Ⓒ Ⓓ
30. **Ⓐ** Ⓑ Ⓒ Ⓓ
31. Ⓐ Ⓑ Ⓒ **Ⓓ**
32. **Ⓐ** Ⓑ Ⓒ Ⓓ
33. Ⓐ Ⓑ **Ⓒ** Ⓓ
34. Ⓐ **Ⓑ** Ⓒ Ⓓ
35. Ⓐ Ⓑ **Ⓒ** Ⓓ
36. Ⓐ **Ⓑ** Ⓒ Ⓓ
37. Ⓐ Ⓑ **Ⓒ** Ⓓ
38. Ⓐ Ⓑ Ⓒ **Ⓓ**
39. Ⓐ **Ⓑ** Ⓒ Ⓓ
40. Ⓐ Ⓑ **Ⓒ** Ⓓ

Fractions, Decimals, and Percents

41. **Ⓐ** Ⓑ Ⓒ Ⓓ
42. Ⓐ Ⓑ **Ⓒ** Ⓓ
43. Ⓐ Ⓑ **Ⓒ** Ⓓ
44. Ⓐ Ⓑ **Ⓒ** Ⓓ

Answer Key (continued)

Mark the space that corresponds to the correct answer.　Form A ✓　Form B ___

---

45. Ⓐ　Ⓑ　**Ⓒ**　Ⓓ
46. **Ⓐ**　Ⓑ　Ⓒ　Ⓓ
47. Ⓐ　Ⓑ　Ⓒ　**Ⓓ**
48. Ⓐ　**Ⓑ**　Ⓒ　Ⓓ
49. Ⓐ　Ⓑ　**Ⓒ**　Ⓓ
50. **Ⓐ**　Ⓑ　Ⓒ　Ⓓ
51. **Ⓐ**　Ⓑ　Ⓒ　Ⓓ

Measurement and Geometry

52. Ⓐ　Ⓑ　**Ⓒ**　Ⓓ
53. Ⓐ　Ⓑ　**Ⓒ**　Ⓓ
54. **Ⓐ**　Ⓑ　Ⓒ　Ⓓ
55. Ⓐ　Ⓑ　Ⓒ　**Ⓓ**
56. Ⓐ　Ⓑ　Ⓒ　**Ⓓ**
57. **Ⓐ**　Ⓑ　Ⓒ　Ⓓ
58. **Ⓐ**　Ⓑ　Ⓒ　Ⓓ
59. Ⓐ　Ⓑ　**Ⓒ**　Ⓓ
60. Ⓐ　Ⓑ　Ⓒ　**Ⓓ**
61. Ⓐ　**Ⓑ**　Ⓒ　Ⓓ
62. Ⓐ　Ⓑ　Ⓒ　**Ⓓ**
63. Ⓐ　Ⓑ　Ⓒ　**Ⓓ**
64. Ⓐ　**Ⓑ**　Ⓒ　Ⓓ
65. Ⓐ　Ⓑ　**Ⓒ**　Ⓓ

66. Ⓐ　Ⓑ　**Ⓒ**　Ⓓ
67. **Ⓐ**　Ⓑ　Ⓒ　Ⓓ
68. Ⓐ　Ⓑ　Ⓒ　**Ⓓ**

Data Analysis and Probability

69. **Ⓐ**　Ⓑ　Ⓒ　Ⓓ
70. Ⓐ　**Ⓑ**　Ⓒ　Ⓓ
71. **Ⓐ**　Ⓑ　Ⓒ　Ⓓ
72. Ⓐ　Ⓑ　**Ⓒ**　Ⓓ
73. Ⓐ　**Ⓑ**　Ⓒ　Ⓓ
74. Ⓐ　Ⓑ　Ⓒ　**Ⓓ**
75. Ⓐ　Ⓑ　**Ⓒ**　Ⓓ
76. Ⓐ　Ⓑ　**Ⓒ**　Ⓓ
77. **Ⓐ**　Ⓑ　Ⓒ　Ⓓ

Problem Solving

78. Ⓐ　Ⓑ　**Ⓒ**　Ⓓ
79. Ⓐ　Ⓑ　Ⓒ　**Ⓓ**
80. Ⓐ　Ⓑ　Ⓒ　**Ⓓ**
81. Ⓐ　Ⓑ　**Ⓒ**　Ⓓ
82. Ⓐ　Ⓑ　Ⓒ　**Ⓓ**
83. Ⓐ　Ⓑ　Ⓒ　**Ⓓ**

Name _____

Answer Key

Mark the space that corresponds to the correct answer. Form A ___ Form B ✓

Numeration, Patterns, and Relationships

1. Ⓐ Ⓑ Ⓒ **Ⓓ**
2. Ⓐ Ⓑ **Ⓒ** Ⓓ
3. Ⓐ Ⓑ Ⓒ **Ⓓ**
4. Ⓐ Ⓑ **Ⓒ** Ⓓ
5. Ⓐ Ⓑ **Ⓒ** Ⓓ
6. Ⓐ Ⓑ Ⓒ **Ⓓ**
7. **Ⓐ** Ⓑ Ⓒ Ⓓ
8. Ⓐ **Ⓑ** Ⓒ Ⓓ
9. Ⓐ **Ⓑ** Ⓒ Ⓓ
10. Ⓐ **Ⓑ** Ⓒ Ⓓ
11. Ⓐ Ⓑ **Ⓒ** Ⓓ
12. Ⓐ Ⓑ **Ⓒ** Ⓓ
13. Ⓐ Ⓑ **Ⓒ** Ⓓ
14. **Ⓐ** Ⓑ Ⓒ Ⓓ
15. Ⓐ Ⓑ **Ⓒ** Ⓓ
16. Ⓐ **Ⓑ** Ⓒ Ⓓ
17. Ⓐ **Ⓑ** Ⓒ Ⓓ

Operations with Whole Numbers

18. Ⓐ Ⓑ **Ⓒ** Ⓓ
19. Ⓐ Ⓑ **Ⓒ** Ⓓ
20. Ⓐ Ⓑ **Ⓒ** Ⓓ
21. Ⓐ Ⓑ **Ⓒ** Ⓓ

22. **Ⓐ** Ⓑ Ⓒ Ⓓ
23. Ⓐ Ⓑ Ⓒ **Ⓓ**
24. **Ⓐ** Ⓑ Ⓒ Ⓓ
25. **Ⓐ** Ⓑ Ⓒ Ⓓ
26. Ⓐ Ⓑ **Ⓒ** Ⓓ
27. Ⓐ Ⓑ **Ⓒ** Ⓓ
28. Ⓐ **Ⓑ** Ⓒ Ⓓ
29. **Ⓐ** Ⓑ Ⓒ Ⓓ
30. Ⓐ Ⓑ **Ⓒ** Ⓓ
31. Ⓐ Ⓑ **Ⓒ** Ⓓ
32. **Ⓐ** Ⓑ Ⓒ Ⓓ
33. Ⓐ Ⓑ **Ⓒ** Ⓓ
34. Ⓐ **Ⓑ** Ⓒ Ⓓ
35. Ⓐ Ⓑ Ⓒ **Ⓓ**
36. Ⓐ Ⓑ Ⓒ **Ⓓ**
37. Ⓐ Ⓑ **Ⓒ** Ⓓ
38. **Ⓐ** Ⓑ Ⓒ Ⓓ
39. Ⓐ Ⓑ **Ⓒ** Ⓓ
40. Ⓐ **Ⓑ** Ⓒ Ⓓ

Fractions, Decimals, and Percents

41. Ⓐ Ⓑ Ⓒ **Ⓓ**
42. Ⓐ Ⓑ Ⓒ **Ⓓ**
43. Ⓐ Ⓑ **Ⓒ** Ⓓ
44. **Ⓐ** Ⓑ Ⓒ Ⓓ

Name _____

Answer Key (continued)

Mark the space that corresponds to the correct answer. Form A ___ Form B ✓

45. Ⓐ **Ⓑ** Ⓒ Ⓓ
46. Ⓐ Ⓑ **Ⓒ** Ⓓ
47. Ⓐ **Ⓑ** Ⓒ Ⓓ
48. Ⓐ Ⓑ **Ⓒ** Ⓓ
49. Ⓐ **Ⓑ** Ⓒ Ⓓ
50. Ⓐ Ⓑ Ⓒ **Ⓓ**
51. **Ⓐ** Ⓑ Ⓒ Ⓓ

Measurement and Geometry

52. Ⓐ **Ⓑ** Ⓒ Ⓓ
53. Ⓐ **Ⓑ** Ⓒ Ⓓ
54. Ⓐ Ⓑ **Ⓒ** Ⓓ
55. **Ⓐ** Ⓑ Ⓒ Ⓓ
56. **Ⓐ** Ⓑ Ⓒ Ⓓ
57. Ⓐ Ⓑ **Ⓒ** Ⓓ
58. Ⓐ **Ⓑ** Ⓒ Ⓓ
59. Ⓐ Ⓑ Ⓒ **Ⓓ**
60. **Ⓐ** Ⓑ Ⓒ Ⓓ
61. **Ⓐ** Ⓑ Ⓒ Ⓓ
62. Ⓐ Ⓑ **Ⓒ** Ⓓ
63. Ⓐ Ⓑ **Ⓒ** Ⓓ
64. Ⓐ Ⓑ **Ⓒ** Ⓓ
65. Ⓐ Ⓑ **Ⓒ** Ⓓ

66. Ⓐ Ⓑ Ⓒ **Ⓓ**
67. Ⓐ Ⓑ Ⓒ **Ⓓ**
68. Ⓐ Ⓑ **Ⓒ** Ⓓ

Data Analysis and Probability

69. Ⓐ Ⓑ **Ⓒ** Ⓓ
70. **Ⓐ** Ⓑ Ⓒ Ⓓ
71. Ⓐ Ⓑ Ⓒ **Ⓓ**
72. Ⓐ Ⓑ Ⓒ **Ⓓ**
73. Ⓐ Ⓑ **Ⓒ** Ⓓ
74. Ⓐ Ⓑ **Ⓒ** Ⓓ
75. Ⓐ **Ⓑ** Ⓒ Ⓓ
76. Ⓐ Ⓑ **Ⓒ** Ⓓ
77. Ⓐ Ⓑ Ⓒ **Ⓓ**

Problem Solving

78. Ⓐ **Ⓑ** Ⓒ Ⓓ
79. Ⓐ Ⓑ Ⓒ **Ⓓ**
80. Ⓐ Ⓑ Ⓒ **Ⓓ**
81. Ⓐ Ⓑ **Ⓒ** Ⓓ
82. Ⓐ Ⓑ Ⓒ **Ⓓ**
83. Ⓐ Ⓑ **Ⓒ** Ⓓ

Name _____

Numeration, Patterns, and Relationships

Read each question. Then mark your answer on the sheet.

1. What is the value of the 2 in 258,364?

   A 20

   B 200

   C 2,000

   D 200,000

2. In standard form

   5,000,000 + 20,000 + 400 + 8

   is equal to which number?

   A 5,200,408

   B 5,020,408

   C 520,408

   D 502,408

3. Which is the word name for 8,700,012?

   A Eight thousand, seven hundred twelve

   B Eight million, seven hundred twelve

   C Eight million, seventy thousand, twelve

   D Eight million, seven hundred thousand, twelve

The table shows the sizes of four countries. Use the table for Questions 4 and 5.

Country	Area in Square Miles
Canada	3,851,800
China	3,705,400
Russia	6,592,800
United States	3,717,796

4. Which of the four countries is the smallest?

   A Canada

   B China

   C Russia

   D United States

5. What is the area of Russia rounded to the nearest hundred thousand square miles?

   A 6,590,000

   B 6,500,000

   C 6,600,000

   D 7,000,000

Read each question. Then mark your answer on the sheet.

6. Which ordered pair names point *M*?

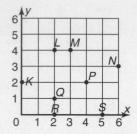

   A (6, 3)   **C** (4, 1)

   B (4, 3)   **D** (3, 4)

7. Find the rule for this table.

n	?
30	20
40	30
50	40
60	50
70	60

   A $n + 10$

   B $n - 10$

   C $10 \times n$

   D $n \div 10$

8. Given the equation $y - 9 = 54$, which of the following is true?

   A $(y - 9) \div 9 = 54 \times 9$

   B $y - 9 + 9 = 54 - 9$

   C $y - 9 + 9 = 54 + 9$

   D $(y - 9) \times 9 = 54 \div 9$

9. In $6m = 24$, what number is represented by *m*?

   A $m = 3$

   B $m = 4$

   C $m = 18$

   D $m = 30$

10. In $y - 4 = 12$, what number is represented by *y*?

   A $y = 3$

   B $y = 8$

   C $y = 16$

   D $y = 48$

11. Which is the missing number?

n	$2 \times n$
2	4
3	6
4	8
5	?

   A 2

   B 9

   C 10

   D 12

Operations with Whole Numbers

Read each question. Then mark your answer on the sheet.

---

12. Victor is adding 358 + 198 by using compensation. He adds 358 + 200 = 558 first. Which of the following should he do next?

   A Add 558 + 2.

   B Subtract 558 − 2.

   C Add 558 + 1.

   D Subtract 558 − 1.

---

13. The library checked out 3,559 books on Monday and 3,328 books on Tuesday. About how many books did the library check out on these two days?

   A About 8,000 books

   B About 7,000 books

   C About 6,000 books

   D About 1,000 books

---

14.   34,675
    + 15,792

   A 49,367

   B 49,467

   C 50,367

   D 50,467

15. Thursday night 39,219 people bought tickets to the baseball game. Friday night 63,516 people bought tickets to the game. About how many more tickets were sold on Friday night?

   A About 20,000 tickets

   B About 30,000 tickets

   C About 90,000 tickets

   D About 100,000 tickets

---

16.   80,700
    − 14,632

   A 65,068

   B 66,068

   C 66,078

   D 76,178

---

17. If you know that 4 × 9 = 36, which number sentence would help you to find the answer to 5 × 9?

   A 36 + 4 = 40

   B 36 + 9 = 45

   C 36 + 8 = 44

   D 36 + 9 = 44

Operations with Whole Numbers (continued)

Read each question. Then mark your answer on the sheet.

---

18. Marta bought three dozen cookies at the bake sale. How many cookies did she buy? There are 12 cookies in a dozen.

    A 3 cookies

    B 30 cookies

    C 36 cookies

    D 48 cookies

---

19. 7)49

    A 8   **C** 5

    B 7   **D** 6

---

20. 15 ÷ 2 =

    A 8 R2

    B 7 R1

    C 6 R1

    D 7 R5

---

21. Nicole bought 8 bags of beads for an art project. Each bag contains 68 beads. About how many beads does she have in all?

    A About 70 beads

    B About 80 beads

    C About 480 beads

    D About 560 beads

---

22. Last year 272 people ran in the marathon. This year twice as many people ran. How many people ran in the marathon this year?

    A 544 people

    B 444 people

    C 454 people

    D 244 people

---

23. A builder has 236 bricks. She wants to make 8 stacks of bricks about the same height. About how many bricks should be in each stack?

    A About 8 bricks

    B About 10 bricks

    C About 20 bricks

    D About 30 bricks

---

24. 3)89

    A 29 R2

    B 28 R1

    C 26 R1

    D 23

38

Name _____

Operations with Whole Numbers (continued)

Read each question. Then mark your answer on the sheet.

25. A grocer ordered 6 frozen turkeys. The turkeys weighed a total of 84 pounds. If each frozen turkey weighed the same number of pounds, how much did each turkey weigh?

   A 54 pounds   C 14 pounds

   B 16 pounds   D 13 pounds

26. A nursery owner has 864 tomato sprouts. If he puts 3 sprouts in each planter, how many planters can he fill?

   A 222 planters

   B 236 planters

   C 268 planters

   D 288 planters

27. Karl and Kendra have 36 chairs to arrange in a rectangular array. Which of the following is NOT a possible array they can use?

   A 3 by 12

   B 4 by 6

   C 4 by 9

   D 6 by 6

28. Which is a prime number?

   A 1   C 27

   B 17   D 39

29. Which list shows all of the factors of 50?

   A 1, 2, 5, 10, 25, 50

   B 1, 2, 5, 10, 50

   C 1, 2, 4, 5, 10, 25, 50

   D 1, 2, 5, 10, 15, 25, 100

30. Each student in Mr. Picard's class brought in 175 soup can labels to trade in for a computer. There are 23 students in the class. How many labels did the class collect in all?

   A 875 labels

   B 3,025 labels

   C 4,025 labels

   D 4,125 labels

31.   46
    × 32

   A 1,472

   B 1,362

   C 872

   D 230

32. What is 30 × 8,000?

   A 2,400

   B 24,000

   C 240,000

   D 2,400,000

Fractions, Decimals, and Percents

Read each question. Then mark your answer on the sheet.

---

33. Which group has exactly $\frac{6}{9}$ white circles?

A

B

C

D

---

34. Ryan bought a pound of cheese. He sliced the cheese into 8 equal pieces. How much does each slice weigh?

A $\frac{1}{10}$ pound

B $\frac{1}{8}$ pound

C $\frac{1}{2}$ pound

D 1 pound

---

35. Which fraction is equivalent to $\frac{2}{5}$?

A $\frac{6}{15}$ C $\frac{6}{10}$

B $\frac{9}{15}$ D $\frac{7}{10}$

---

36. What is $\frac{14}{18}$ in simplest form?

A $\frac{7}{8}$ C $\frac{2}{3}$

B $\frac{7}{9}$ D $\frac{8}{7}$

---

37. Which mixed number describes the shaded areas?

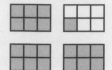

A $3\frac{1}{6}$

B $3\frac{1}{4}$

C $3\frac{1}{2}$

D $3\frac{5}{6}$

---

38. Which letter is at $2\frac{1}{4}$ on the number line?

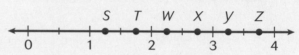

A T   C V

B U   D W

---

39. A carpenter has boards that are $\frac{3}{4}$ yard, $\frac{1}{2}$ yard, $\frac{1}{3}$ yard, and $\frac{7}{8}$ yard long. Which lists the lengths of the boards from greatest to least?

A $\frac{3}{4}, \frac{7}{8}, \frac{1}{2}, \frac{1}{3}$

B $\frac{3}{4}, \frac{7}{8}, \frac{1}{3}, \frac{1}{2}$

C $\frac{7}{8}, \frac{1}{2}, \frac{3}{4}, \frac{1}{3}$

D $\frac{7}{8}, \frac{3}{4}, \frac{1}{2}, \frac{1}{3}$

Fractions, Decimals, and Percents (continued)

Read each question. Then mark your answer on the sheet.

---

40. Mario spent $18.78 at the store. He gave the clerk $20. Which set of bills and coins could be his change?

  A 2 pennies, 2 dimes, 1 dollar

  B 3 pennies, 1 quarter, 1 dollar

  C 2 pennies, 2 dimes, 2 dollars

  D 3 pennies, 1 quarter, 2 dollars

---

41. $3.62 is the same as

  A 3 dollars + 6 dimes + 2 pennies

  B 3 dollars + 2 dimes + 6 pennies

  C 6 dollars + 2 dimes + 3 pennies

  D 2 dollars + 6 dimes + 3 pennies

---

42. What is the place value of 2 in 35.24?

  A Tens

  B Ones

  C Tenths

  D Hundredths

---

43. Which set of decimals is ordered from least to greatest?

  A 2.7, 2.72, 2.68, 2.65

  B 2.68, 2.65, 2.7, 2.72

  C 2.65, 2.68, 2.72, 2.7

  D 2.65, 2.68, 2.7, 2.72

---

44. Which decimal is equal to $\frac{7}{100}$?

  A 0.07

  B 0.70

  C 0.7100

  D 7.100

---

45. Which point is located at 3.27?

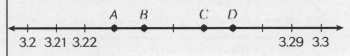

  A Point *A*   **C** Point *C*

  B Point *B*   **D** Point *D*

---

46. Which shows 27.49 rounded to the nearest whole number?

  A 27

  B 27.4

  C 27.5

  D 28

---

47. Which mixed number is located at Point *S*?

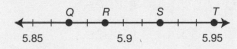

  A $5\frac{7}{10}$

  B $5\frac{9}{10}$

  C $5\frac{92}{100}$

  D $6\frac{2}{10}$

Fractions, Decimals, and Percents (continued)

Read each question. Then mark your answer on the sheet.

48. What is $\frac{5}{6} - \frac{2}{3}$?

A $\frac{3}{3}$

B $\frac{3}{6}$

C $\frac{1}{6}$

D $\frac{2}{18}$

49. On Monday, Lacy ran $\frac{2}{5}$ mile. On Tuesday, she ran $\frac{3}{10}$ mile. How far did she run all together?

A $\frac{12}{15}$ mile

B $\frac{7}{10}$ mile

C $\frac{5}{10}$ mile

D $\frac{4}{10}$ mile

50. Mateo is 51.25 inches tall. His brother is 37.75 inches tall. About how much taller is Mateo than his brother?

A About 10 inches

B About 20 inches

C About 80 inches

D About 90 inches

51. What is 3.7 + 4.51?

A 4.88   C 48.8

B 8.21   D 82.1

52. Misty bought 2.35 pounds of apples and 1.84 pounds of oranges. How many more pounds of apples than oranges did she buy?

A 0.41 pound

B 0.51 pound

C 1.41 pounds

D 1.51 pounds

53. Mary's watering can holds 3.4 liters of liquid plant food. She filled the can three times when she watered yesterday. How many liters of liquid plant food did she use?

A 9.2 liters   C 92 liters

B 10.2 liters   D 102 liters

54. Mrs. Kuhn bought 8.75 yards of material. She needed to divide this evenly among 7 children. How many yards of material did each child get?

A 1.05 yards   C 1.5 yards

B 1.25 yards   D 1.75 yards

Measurement and Geometry

Read each question. Then mark your answer on the sheet.

---

55. Which is a side view of the figure?

A

B

C

D

56. Which solid will the net form?

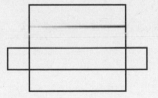

A Square pyramid

B Rectangular prism

C Cone

D Cube

57. Describe the pair of lines.

A Perpendicular lines

B Parallel lines

C Intersecting lines

D Rays

58. What type of angle is shown?

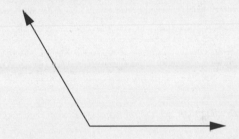

A Obtuse

B Acute

C Right

D Straight

59. Which triangle has an angle with a measure greater than 90 degrees?

A Right triangle

B Acute triangle

C Equilateral triangle

D Obtuse triangle

Measurement and Geometry (continued)

Read each question. Then mark your answer on the sheet.

60. **Which quadrilateral has only
one pair of parallel sides?**

    A Rectangle

    B Square

    C Trapezoid

    D Rhombus

61. **What is the measure of angle
    LMN?**

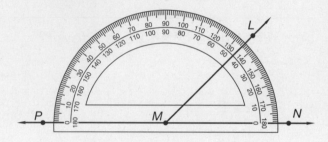

    A 45°

    B 55°

    C 125°

    D 135°

62. **Which angle measure and turn
    describes the rotation?**

    A 90° or $\frac{1}{4}$ turn

    B 180° or $\frac{1}{2}$ turn

    C 270° or $\frac{3}{4}$ turn

    D 360° or full turn

63. **Which transformation can be
    used to show the two figures
    are congruent?**

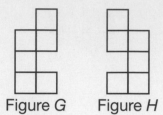

    Figure *G*   Figure *H*

    A Rotation

    B Reflection

    C Translation

    D Reflection and translation

64. **Which figure has rotational
    symmetry?**

    A

    B

    C

    D

Measurement and Geometry (continued)

Read each question. Then mark your answer on the sheet.

65. Which letter has **NO** line of symmetry?

   A The letter H

   B The letter I

   C The letter L

   D The letter D

66. Which is the best estimate for the length of a child's wagon?

   A 1 inch

   B 1 yard

   C 1 mile

   D 10 yards

67. If you buy 2 containers of grape juice, how many cups of grape juice will you have?

   A 1 cup

   B 4 cups

   C 2 cups

   D 8 cups

Grape Juice 1 pint

68. Which is the best estimate for the mass of a cell phone?

   A 100 grams

   B 1 gram

   C 100 kilograms

   D 1 kilogram

69. Which length is greatest?

   A 200 centimeters

   B 8 decimeters

   C 2,000 meters

   D 1 kilometer

70. Luis's watch shows 3:32. His swim practice starts in 35 minutes. What time does swim practice start?

   A 3:47   **C** 4:17

   B 4:07   **D** 4:47

71. 52 weeks = 1 year
    1 year 6 weeks = ■ days

   A 406   **C** 314

   B 371   **D** 58

72. What is the temperature after a decrease of 12°F from the temperature shown?

   A 63°F   **C** 55°F

   B 60°F   **D** 12°F

Read each question. Then mark your answer on the sheet.

73. **Find the perimeter of the
rectangle. You can use the
formula *P = 2ℓ + 2w*.**

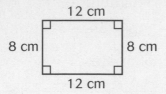

12 cm

8 cm   8 cm

12 cm

A 4 cm   C 28 cm

B 20 cm   D 40 cm

74. **What is the area of the triangle?**

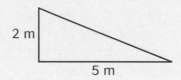

2 m

5 m

A 5 square meters

B 7 square meters

C 10 square meters

D 20 square meters

75. **Jack is installing new carpet in
the family room shown. Which is
the area of the family room?**

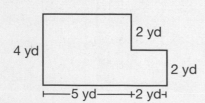

2 yd

4 yd

2 yd

5 yd   2 yd

A 15 square yd C 24 square yd

B 22 square yd D 28 square yd

**Use the figure below to answer
Questions 76 and 77.**

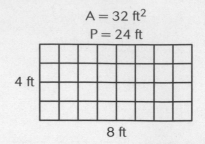

A = 32 ft²
P = 24 ft

4 ft

8 ft

76. **Which are the dimensions of
another rectangle with the same
area as the given rectangle?**

A 16 ft × 2 ft

B 6 ft × 4 ft

C 12 ft × 2 ft

D 16 ft × 16 ft

77. **Which are the dimensions
of a rectangle with the same
perimeter as the given rectangle?**

A 6 ft × 4 ft

B 12 ft × 12 ft

C 9 ft × 3 ft

D 8 ft × 3 ft

78. **What is the volume
of the figure?**

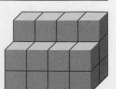

A 12 cubic units

B 20 cubic units

C 24 cubic units

D 28 cubic units

Data Analysis and Probability

Read each question. Then mark your answer on the sheet.

---

79. A scientist at a national park counted the animals she saw. The scientist made the bar graph shown below.

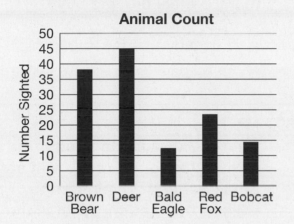

Animal Count

Which was sighted more than 15 times, but less than 35 times?

A Deer   **C** Bald Eagle

B Bobcat   **D** Red Fox

---

80. What fraction of the students surveyed preferred swimming?

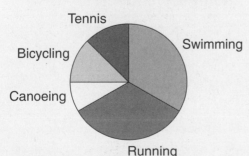

Favorite Summer Activities

A $\frac{1}{2}$ **C** $\frac{1}{4}$

B $\frac{1}{3}$ **D** $\frac{3}{4}$

Use the stem-and-leaf plot for Questions 81 and 82.

Points Earned	
Stem	Leaves
2	5, 8, 8, 8, 9
3	0, 1, 5, 6, 8, 9

81. What is the range of points earned?

A 39   **C** 14

B 29   **D** 5

---

82. What is the mode?

A 28   **C** 35

B 30   **D** 39

---

83. What is the mean of this set of data?

7, 2, 4, 7, 6, 7, 2

A 5   **C** 6

B 5.5   **D** 7

---

84. A bag contains 5 red marbles, 3 blue marbles, and 2 purple marbles. What is the probability of getting a blue marble if you reach in and take one without looking?

A $\frac{3}{10}$ **C** $\frac{1}{2}$

B $\frac{3}{7}$ **D** $\frac{3}{5}$

Problem Solving

Read each question. Then mark your answer on the sheet.

85. Lena caught 8 fish and Sven caught 2 fish. The fish weighed about 2 pounds each. What hidden question can you use to find how much the fish weighed in all?

   A What is the weight of all the fish?

   B How many more fish did Lena catch than Sven?

   C What kind of fish did they catch?

   D How many fish did they catch altogether?

86. Joan is looking for an office on the second floor of a medical building. The first office is numbered 203, the next office is numbered 213, and the third office is numbered 223. If the pattern continues, what is the number of the sixth office?

   A 233   C 253

   B 243   D 263

87. Ida collects 139 shells and gives 21 of them to Joe. Which number sentence shows the number of shells Ida has?

   A $139 + 21 = n$ C $139 \div 21 = n$

   B $139 - 21 = n$ D $139 \times 21 = n$

88. Samuel's mom bought a total of 24 bagels and muffins at the bakery. She bought three times as many bagels as muffins. How many bagels did she buy?

   A 6 bagels   C 16 bagels

   B 12 bagels   D 18 bagels

89. Mr. Tyson needs to catch the train at 7:05 A.M. He needs 45 minutes to get ready and eat breakfast and 20 minutes to walk to the station. What is the latest time he can wake up and arrive at the station in time to catch the train?

   A 5:45 A.M.

   B 6:00 A.M.

   C 6:15 A.M.

   D 6:20 A.M.

90. Which statement is true about the figure shown?

   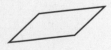

   A It is a pentagon.

   B It is a triangle.

   C It has two pairs of parallel sides.

   D It has no parallel sides.

Numeration, Patterns, and Relationships

Read each question. Then mark your answer on the sheet.

1. What is the value of the 5 in the number 152,309?

   A 50,000

   B 5,000

   C 500

   D 50

2. In standard form

   80,000,000 + 700,000 + 50,000 + 6,000 + 500 + 3

   is equal to which number?

   A 87,056,503

   B 80,756,503

   C 8,756,503

   D 8,750,653

3. What is the word name for 4,700,050?

   A Forty-seven thousand, fifty

   B Forty-seven million, fifty

   C Four million, seventy thousand, fifty

   D Four million, seven hundred thousand, fifty

The table shows the greatest distance of the first four planets from the sun.

Planet	Distance in Miles
Earth	94,500,000
Mars	154,900,000
Mercury	43,400,000
Venus	67,600,000

4. Which of the four planets is farthest from the sun?

   A Earth

   B Mars

   C Mercury

   D Venus

5. Earth's average distance from the sun is 92,955,807 miles. What is this distance rounded to the nearest ten thousand miles?

   A 93,000,000

   B 92,960,000

   C 92,950,000

   D 92,900,000

Read each question. Then mark your answer on the sheet.

6. **Which ordered pair names point *P*?**

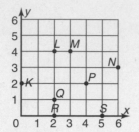

A (4, 2)   C (4, 0)

B (2, 4)   D (2, 0)

7. **Find the rule for this table.**

n	?
5	20
10	40
12	48
15	60
20	80

A $4 \times n$

B $n \div 4$

C $n + 4$

D $n - 4$

8. **Given the equation $y + 7 = 32$, which of the following is true?**

A $(y + 7) \div 7 = 32 \times 7$

B $y + 7 - 7 = 32 - 7$

C $y + 7 - 7 = 32 + 7$

D $(y + 7) \times 7 = 32 \div 7$

9. **In $\frac{n}{4} = 5$, what number is represented by *n*?**

A $n = 1$

B $n = 9$

C $n = 20$

D $n = 54$

10. **In $y + 5 = 16$, what number is represented by *y*?**

A $y = 3$

B $y = 11$

C $y = 21$

D $y = 80$

11. **Which is the missing number?**

n	*n* − 2
2	0
3	1
4	2
5	?

A 6

B 5

C 4

D 3

Operations with Whole Numbers

Read each question. Then mark your answer on the sheet.

12. **Megan is subtracting 473 − 299 by using compensation. First she subtracts 473 − 300 = 173. Which of the following should she do next?**

   A Add 173 + 2.

   B Subtract 173 − 2.

   C Add 173 + 1.

   D Subtract 173 − 1.

13. **There were 5,212 movie tickets sold on Friday night and 3,742 tickets sold on Saturday night. About how many movie tickets were sold on these two days?**

   A About 9,000 movie tickets

   B About 8,000 movie tickets

   C About 7,000 movie tickets

   D About 1,000 movie tickets

14.   **47,286
      + 15,472**

   A 52,928

   B 53,028

   C 62,028

   D 62,758

15. **Zane scored 47,421 points on a video game. Skully scored 74,762 points. About how many more points did Skully score than Zane?**

   A About 20,000 points

   B About 30,000 points

   C About 90,000 points

   D About 100,000 points

16.   **70,900
      − 15,756**

   A 65,254

   B 55,254

   C 55,154

   D 55,144

17. **if you knew 4 × 5 = 20, which number sentence could you use to find the answer to 5 × 5?**

   A 20 + 4 = 24

   B 25 + 5 = 30

   C 20 + 6 = 26

   D 20 + 5 = 25

Operations with Whole Numbers (continued)

Read each question. Then mark your answer on the sheet.

---

18. Tammy bought two dozen eggs. How many eggs did she buy? There are 12 eggs in a dozen.

    A 2 eggs

    B 12 eggs

    C 24 eggs

    D 36 eggs

---

19. $7\overline{)35}$

    A 6

    B 7

    C 9

    D 5

---

20. $16 \div 3 =$

    A 4 R2

    B 5 R1

    C 5 R2

    D 7 R3

---

21. Juan bought 7 packs of trading cards. Each pack has 28 cards. About how many cards does Juan have in all?

    A About 30 cards

    B About 70 cards

    C About 140 cards

    D About 210 cards

---

22. Alexa has 3 boxes of labels. There are 220 labels in each box. How many labels does she have in all?

    A 223 labels

    B 620 labels

    C 660 labels

    D 663 labels

---

23. There are 578 party favors in a bag. The favors will be equally divided among 9 party guests. About how many favors will each guest get?

    A About 100 favors

    B About 80 favors

    C About 60 favors

    D About 10 favors

---

24. $4\overline{)71}$

    A 15 R1

    B 16 R3

    C 16 R6

    D 17 R3

Operations with Whole Numbers (continued)

Read each question. Then mark your answer on the sheet.

25. There are 64 crackers in a box. Cecil puts 4 crackers in a snack bag. How many snack bags does Cecil need if he uses all of the crackers in the box?

    A 10 bags   C 16 bags

    B 12 bags   D 18 bags

26. The fan factory ordered 948 fan blades. If 4 blades are needed for each fan, how many fans can be made?

    A 238 fans

    B 237 fans

    C 227 fans

    D 212 fans

27. Ms. Thompson's class has 24 sculptures to display in a rectangular array. Which of the following is NOT a possible array they can use?

    A 3 by 8

    B 4 by 6

    C 3 by 6

    D 2 by 12

28. Which number is a prime number?

    A 35   C 57

    B 49   D 61

29. Which list shows all of the factors of 45?

    A 1, 5, 9, 45

    B 1, 3, 6, 9, 12, 45

    C 1, 3, 5, 9, 15, 45

    D 1, 5, 7, 9, 45

30. A bakery makes and sells 192 bagels each day. How many bagels are sold in a month with 28 days?

    A 5,386 bagels

    B 5,376 bagels

    C 1,920 bagels

    D 1,536 bagels

31. $$\begin{array}{r} 54 \\ \times\ 26 \\ \hline \end{array}$$

    A 432

    B 1,384

    C 1,404

    D 11,124

32. What is $40 \times 3,000$?

    A 1,200

    B 12,000

    C 120,000

    D 1,200,000

Fractions, Decimals, and Percents

Read each question. Then mark your answer on the sheet.

---

33. Which group has exactly $\frac{7}{10}$ white circles?

A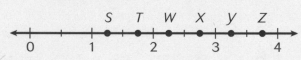

B

C

D

---

34. Mrs. Lopez has 1 apple. She wants her 4 children to share the apple equally. How much will each child get?

A $\frac{1}{4}$ apple   **C** $\frac{3}{4}$ apple

B $\frac{1}{2}$ apple   **D** 4 apples

---

35. Which fraction is equivalent to $\frac{3}{4}$?

A $\frac{3}{8}$ **C** $\frac{12}{16}$

B $\frac{5}{8}$ **D** $\frac{15}{16}$

---

36. What is $\frac{10}{12}$ in simplest form?

A $\frac{5}{3}$ **C** $\frac{1}{2}$

B $\frac{5}{6}$ **D** $\frac{6}{5}$

---

37. Which mixed number describes the shaded areas?

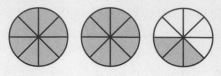

A $3\frac{3}{8}$ **C** $2\frac{1}{2}$

B $2\frac{5}{8}$ **D** $2\frac{3}{8}$

---

38. Which letter is at $2\frac{3}{4}$ on the number line?

$$S \quad T \quad W \quad X \quad Y \quad Z$$

0   1   2   3   4

A W **C** Y

B X **D** Z

---

39. A recipe calls for $\frac{1}{3}$ cup of sugar, $\frac{5}{6}$ cup of flour, $\frac{1}{2}$ cup of butter, and $\frac{2}{3}$ cup of apples. Which lists the amounts of the ingredients from greatest to least?

A $\frac{5}{6}, \frac{2}{3}, \frac{1}{2}, \frac{1}{3}$

B $\frac{5}{6}, \frac{1}{2}, \frac{2}{3}, \frac{1}{3}$

C $\frac{2}{3}, \frac{5}{6}, \frac{1}{2}, \frac{1}{3}$

D $\frac{2}{3}, \frac{5}{6}, \frac{1}{3}, \frac{1}{2}$

Fractions, Decimals, and Percents (continued)

Read each question. Then mark your answer on the sheet.

---

40. Mindy spent $17.74 at the store. She gave the clerk $20. Which set of bills and coins could be her change?

A 1 penny, 1 quarter, 2 dollars

B 4 pennies, 2 dimes, 2 dollars

C 1 penny, 2 dimes, 2 dollars

D 1 penny, 1 quarter, 3 dollars

---

41. $8.45 is the same as

A 8 dollars + 4 dimes + 5 pennies

B 8 dollars + 5 dimes + 4 pennies

C 4 dollars + 8 dimes + 5 pennies

D 5 dollars + 4 dimes + 8 pennies

---

42. What is the place value of 5 in 12.45?

A Tens

B Ones

C Tenths

D Hundredths

---

43. Which set of decimals is ordered from least to greatest?

A 3.4, 3.41, 3.46, 3.14

B 3.14, 3.41, 3.46, 3.4

C 3.14, 3.4, 3.41, 3.46

D 3.4, 3.41, 3.14, 3.46

---

44. Which decimal is equal to $\frac{9}{100}$?

A 0.09

B 0.90

C 0.9100

D 9.100

---

45. Which point is located at 3.24?

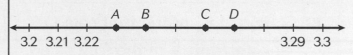

A Point A   C Point C

B Point B   D Point D

---

46. Which shows 35.78 rounded to the nearest whole number?

A 35

B 35.7

C 35.8

D 36

---

47. Which mixed number is located at Point M?

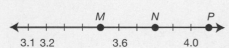

A $3\frac{7}{10}$

B $3\frac{5}{10}$

C $3\frac{7}{100}$

D $3\frac{5}{100}$

Fractions, Decimals, and Percents (continued)

Read each question. Then mark your answer on the sheet.

---

48. What is $\frac{5}{12} + \frac{1}{3}$?

    A $\frac{6}{12}$

    B $\frac{7}{12}$

    C $\frac{8}{12}$

    D $\frac{9}{12}$

---

49. Jason ate $\frac{1}{4}$ of the fruit salad and Tony ate $\frac{3}{8}$ of the fruit salad. How much more did Tony eat than Jason?

    A $\frac{1}{8}$ more

    B $\frac{2}{8}$ more

    C $\frac{4}{8}$ more

    D $\frac{5}{8}$ more

---

50. Kellie's paper airplane flew 68.75 feet. Trudy's paper airplane flew 42.25 feet. About how much farther did Kellie's plane fly than Trudy's?

    A 30 feet

    B 40 feet

    C 100 feet

    D 110 feet

---

51. What is 2.8 + 5.64?

    A 5.92   C 8.44

    B 7.44   D 84.4

---

52. Kelly bought 1.94 pounds of walnuts and 2.16 pounds of peanuts. How many more pounds of peanuts than walnuts did she buy?

    A 0.22 pound

    B 0.82 pound

    C 2.2 pounds

    D 8.2 pounds

---

53. Melinda drives a total of 7.9 miles each day to get to and from work. How many miles does Melinda drive in 5 days?

    A 39.5 miles

    B 40.5 miles

    C 395 miles

    D 405 miles

---

54. Brian and Gregory bought 5.9 pounds of dried apple chips. If they divide the dried fruit evenly between themselves, how much dried fruit does each boy get?

    A 2.95 lb   C 5.9 lb

    B 3.95 lb   D 29.5 lb

Measurement and Geometry

Read each question. Then mark your answer on the sheet.

---

55. Which is the top view of the figure?

A

B

C

D

---

56. Which solid will the net form?

A Triangular pyramid

B Rectangular prism

C Triangular prism

D Square pyramid

---

57. Describe the pair of lines.

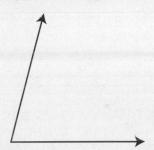

A Parallel lines

B Perpendicular lines

C Rays

D Line segments

---

58. What type of angle is shown?

A Obtuse

B Acute

C Right

D Straight

---

59. Which triangle has three congruent sides?

A Obtuse triangle

B Scalene triangle

C Equilateral triangle

D Right triangle

Measurement and Geometry (continued)

Read each question. Then mark your answer on the sheet.

---

60. Which quadrilateral always has 4 congruent sides and 4 right angles?

A Trapezoid

B Rectangle

C Rhombus

D Square

---

61. What is the measure of angle *PML*?

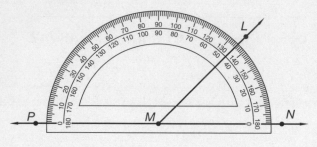

A 45°   **C** 125°

B 55°   **D** 135°

---

62. Which angle measure and turn describes the rotation?

A 90° or $\frac{1}{4}$ turn

B 180° or $\frac{1}{2}$ turn

C 270° or $\frac{3}{4}$ turn

D 360° or full turn

---

63. Which transformation can be used to show the two figures are congruent?

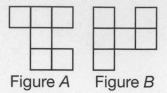

Figure *A*   Figure *B*

A Rotation

B Reflection

C Translation

D Reflection and translation

---

64. Which shape has rotational symmetry?

A

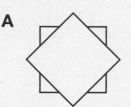

B

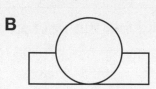

C

D

Measurement and Geometry (continued)

Read each question. Then mark your answer on the sheet.

65. **Which letter has more than one
line of symmetry?**

A The letter M

B The letter T

C The letter E

D The letter O

66. **Which is the best estimate for
the distance walked in 2 hours?**

A 8 inches

B 8 yards

C 8 miles

D 80 miles

67. **If you buy 8 bottles of spring
water, how many gallons will
you have?**

A 1 gallon

B 2 gallons

C 4 gallons

D 8 gallons

Spring
Water
1 quart

68. **Which is the best estimate for
the mass of a football player?**

A 1 kilogram

B 1 gram

C 100 kilograms

D 100 grams

69. **Which length is greatest?**

A 2,000 centimeters

B 2 meters

C 20 centimeters

D 200 millimeters

70. **Chris's watch shows 4:52. He
wants to see a movie that starts
in 30 minutes. What time does
the movie start?**

A 4:22   C 5:22

B 5:12   D 5:32

71. **52 weeks = 1 year
4 years = ■ weeks**

A 208   C 52

B 156   D 28

72. **What is the temperature after
a decrease of 21°F from the
temperature shown?**

A 43°F   C 9°F

B 32°F   D 7°F

Read each question. Then mark your answer on the sheet.

73. **Find the perimeter of the rectangle. You can use the formula $P = 2\ell + 2w$.**

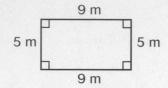

9 m
5 m   5 m
9 m

A 4 m   C 28 m

B 14 m   D 45 m

74. **What is the area of the triangle?**

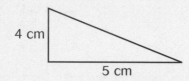

4 cm
5 cm

A 9 square centimeters

B 10 square centimeters

C 20 square centimeters

D 40 square centimeters

75. **Ginger is installing tile in the bathroom shown below. Which is the area of the bathroom?**

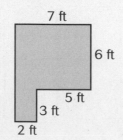

7 ft
6 ft
5 ft
3 ft
2 ft

A 41 square feet

B 48 square feet

C 63 square feet

D 99 square feet

Use the rectangle below to answer Questions 76 and 77.

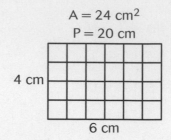

$A = 24$ cm^2
$P = 20$ cm
4 cm
6 cm

76. **Which are the dimensions of another rectangle with the same area as the rectangle above?**

A 3 cm × 4 cm

B 2 cm × 6 cm

C 4 cm × 5 cm

D 3 cm × 8 cm

77. **Which are the dimensions of a rectangle with the same perimeter as the rectangle above?**

A 2 cm by 9 cm

B 5 cm by 4 cm

C 3 cm by 7 cm

D 5 cm by 5 cm

78. **What is the volume of the figure?**

A 16 cubic units

B 20 cubic units

C 24 cubic units

D 28 cubic units

60

Data Analysis and Probability

Read each question. Then mark your answer on the sheet.

79. A scientist at a national park counted the animals she saw. The scientist made the bar graph shown below.

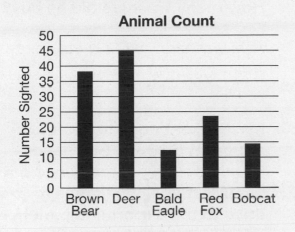

Which was sighted more than 25 times, but less than 45 times?

A Deer

B Bobcat

C Brown Bear

D Red Fox

80. What fraction of the students surveyed preferred bicycling and tennis combined?

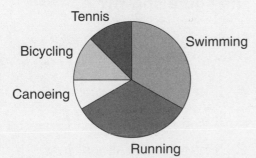

A $\frac{1}{4}$

B $\frac{2}{3}$

C $\frac{3}{4}$

D $\frac{1}{2}$

Use the stem-and-leaf plot for Questions 81 and 82.

Points Earned	
Stem	Leaves
4	5, 8, 8, 8, 9
6	0, 1, 5, 6, 8, 9

81. What is the range of points earned?

A 114

B 60

C 24

D 4

82. What is the mode?

A 48

B 45

C 8

D 6

83. What is the mean of this set of data?

8, 3, 5, 8, 7, 8, 3

A 6

B 7

C 8

D 9

84. A bag contains 3 red marbles, 1 blue marble, and 4 purple marbles. What is the probability of getting a red marble if you reach in and take one without looking?

A $\frac{3}{8}$

B $\frac{1}{2}$

C $\frac{3}{5}$

D $\frac{3}{4}$

Problem Solving

Read each question. Then mark your answer on the sheet.

---

85. George bought 2 T-shirts and Ellen bought 3 T-shirts. The T-shirts cost $7 each. What hidden question can you use to find how much they spent?

  A What is the cost of 10 T-shirts?

  B How many more T-shirts did Ellen buy than George?

  C What color are the T-shirts?

  D How many T-shirts did they buy altogether?

---

86. The first house on Mark's paper route has house number 414, his next house is numbered 424. The third house is numbered 434. If the pattern continues, what is the house number of the fifth house?

  A 436   **C** 454

  B 444   **D** 464

---

87. The first day of the sale, 275 T-shirts were sold. The next day, 15 more T-shirts were sold. Which number sentence shows how many T-shirts were sold the second day?

  A $275 + 15 = n$

  B $275 - 15 = n$

  C $275 \div 15 = n$

  D $275 \times 15 = n$

---

88. Taylor's dad bought a total of 42 nuts and washers at the hardware store. He bought twice as many washers as nuts. How many washers did he buy?

  A 7 washers   **C** 21 washers

  B 14 washers   **D** 28 washers

---

89. Ms. Barker needs to be at the airport at 6:35 A.M. She needs 50 minutes to get ready and eat breakfast and 45 minutes to drive to the airport and park her car. What is the latest time she can wake up to be at the airport on time?

  A 4:45 A.M.

  B 5:10 A.M.

  C 5:00 A.M.

  D 5:20 A.M.

---

90. Which statement is true about the figure shown?

  A It is a pentagon.

  B It is a rectangle.

  C It has no parallel sides.

  D It has exactly one pair of parallel sides.

Name _____

Answer Sheet

Mark the space that corresponds to the correct answer.   Form A ___ Form B

Numeration, Patterns, and Relationships

1. (A) (B) (C) (D)
2. (A) (B) (C) (D)
3. (A) (B) (C) (D)
4. (A) (B) (C) (D)
5. (A) (B) (C) (D)
6. (A) (B) (C) (D)
7. (A) (B) (C) (D)
8. (A) (B) (C) (D)
9. (A) (B) (C) (D)
10. (A) (B) (C) (D)
11. (A) (B) (C) (D)

Operations with Whole Numbers

12. (A) (B) (C) (D)
13. (A) (B) (C) (D)
14. (A) (B) (C) (D)
15. (A) (B) (C) (D)
16. (A) (B) (C) (D)
17. (A) (B) (C) (D)
18. (A) (B) (C) (D)
19. (A) (B) (C) (D)
20. (A) (B) (C) (D)
21. (A) (B) (C) (D)
22. (A) (B) (C) (D)

23. (A) (B) (C) (D)
24. (A) (B) (C) (D)
25. (A) (B) (C) (D)
26. (A) (B) (C) (D)
27. (A) (B) (C) (D)
28. (A) (B) (C) (D)
29. (A) (B) (C) (D)
30. (A) (B) (C) (D)
31. (A) (B) (C) (D)
32. (A) (B) (C) (D)

Fractions, Decimals, and Percents

33. (A) (B) (C) (D)
34. (A) (B) (C) (D)
35. (A) (B) (C) (D)
36. (A) (B) (C) (D)
37. (A) (B) (C) (D)
38. (A) (B) (C) (D)
39. (A) (B) (C) (D)
40. (A) (B) (C) (D)
41. (A) (B) (C) (D)
42. (A) (B) (C) (D)
43. (A) (B) (C) (D)
44. (A) (B) (C) (D)
45. (A) (B) (C) (D)

Answer Sheet (continued)

Mark the space that corresponds to the correct answer.   Form A ____ Form B ____

46. (A) (B) (C) (D)   70. (A) (B) (C) (D)

47. (A) (B) (C) (D)   71. (A) (B) (C) (D)

48. (A) (B) (C) (D)   72. (A) (B) (C) (D)

49. (A) (B) (C) (D)   73. (A) (B) (C) (D)

50. (A) (B) (C) (D)   74. (A) (B) (C) (D)

51. (A) (B) (C) (D)   75. (A) (B) (C) (D)

52. (A) (B) (C) (D)   76. (A) (B) (C) (D)

53. (A) (B) (C) (D)   77. (A) (B) (C) (D)

54. (A) (B) (C) (D)   78. (A) (B) (C) (D)

Measurement and Geometry

55. (A) (B) (C) (D)

56. (A) (B) (C) (D)

57. (A) (B) (C) (D)

58. (A) (B) (C) (D)

59. (A) (B) (C) (D)

60. (A) (B) (C) (D)

61. (A) (B) (C) (D)

62. (A) (B) (C) (D)

63. (A) (B) (C) (D)

64. (A) (B) (C) (D)

65. (A) (B) (C) (D)

66. (A) (B) (C) (D)

67. (A) (B) (C) (D)

68. (A) (B) (C) (D)

69. (A) (B) (C) (D)

Data Analysis and Probability

79. (A) (B) (C) (D)

80. (A) (B) (C) (D)

81. (A) (B) (C) (D)

82. (A) (B) (C) (D)

83. (A) (B) (C) (D)

84. (A) (B) (C) (D)

Problem Solving

85. (A) (B) (C) (D)

86. (A) (B) (C) (D)

87. (A) (B) (C) (D)

88. (A) (B) (C) (D)

89. (A) (B) (C) (D)

90. (A) (B) (C) (D)

Name _____

Answer Key

Mark the space that corresponds to the correct answer.   Form A ✓   Form B ___

Numeration, Patterns, and Relationships

1. Ⓐ Ⓑ Ⓒ **Ⓓ**
2. Ⓐ **Ⓑ** Ⓒ Ⓓ
3. Ⓐ Ⓑ Ⓒ **Ⓓ**
4. Ⓐ **Ⓑ** Ⓒ Ⓓ
5. Ⓐ Ⓑ **Ⓒ** Ⓓ
6. Ⓐ Ⓑ Ⓒ **Ⓓ**
7. Ⓐ **Ⓑ** Ⓒ Ⓓ
8. Ⓐ Ⓑ **Ⓒ** Ⓓ
9. Ⓐ **Ⓑ** Ⓒ Ⓓ
10. Ⓐ Ⓑ **Ⓒ** Ⓓ
11. Ⓐ Ⓑ **Ⓒ** Ⓓ

Operations with Whole Numbers

12. Ⓐ **Ⓑ** Ⓒ Ⓓ
13. Ⓐ **Ⓑ** Ⓒ Ⓓ
14. Ⓐ Ⓑ Ⓒ **Ⓓ**
15. **Ⓐ** Ⓑ Ⓒ Ⓓ
16. Ⓐ **Ⓑ** Ⓒ Ⓓ
17. Ⓐ **Ⓑ** Ⓒ Ⓓ
18. Ⓐ Ⓑ **Ⓒ** Ⓓ
19. Ⓐ **Ⓑ** Ⓒ Ⓓ
20. Ⓐ **Ⓑ** Ⓒ Ⓓ
21. Ⓐ Ⓑ Ⓒ **Ⓓ**
22. **Ⓐ** Ⓑ Ⓒ Ⓓ

23. Ⓐ Ⓑ Ⓒ **Ⓓ**
24. **Ⓐ** Ⓑ Ⓒ Ⓓ
25. Ⓐ Ⓑ **Ⓒ** Ⓓ
26. Ⓐ Ⓑ Ⓒ **Ⓓ**
27. Ⓐ **Ⓑ** Ⓒ Ⓓ
28. Ⓐ **Ⓑ** Ⓒ Ⓓ
29. **Ⓐ** Ⓑ Ⓒ Ⓓ
30. Ⓐ Ⓑ **Ⓒ** Ⓓ
31. **Ⓐ** Ⓑ Ⓒ Ⓓ
32. Ⓐ Ⓑ **Ⓒ** Ⓓ

Fractions, Decimals, and Percents

33. Ⓐ Ⓑ **Ⓒ** Ⓓ
34. Ⓐ **Ⓑ** Ⓒ Ⓓ
35. **Ⓐ** Ⓑ Ⓒ Ⓓ
36. Ⓐ **Ⓑ** Ⓒ Ⓓ
37. **Ⓐ** Ⓑ Ⓒ Ⓓ
38. Ⓐ Ⓑ Ⓒ **Ⓓ**
39. Ⓐ Ⓑ Ⓒ **Ⓓ**
40. **Ⓐ** Ⓑ Ⓒ Ⓓ
41. **Ⓐ** Ⓑ Ⓒ Ⓓ
42. Ⓐ Ⓑ **Ⓒ** Ⓓ
43. Ⓐ Ⓑ Ⓒ **Ⓓ**
44. **Ⓐ** Ⓑ Ⓒ Ⓓ
45. Ⓐ Ⓑ Ⓒ **Ⓓ**

Name _____

Answer Key (continued)

Mark the space that corresponds to the correct answer.   Form A ✓   Form B ___

46. (A) (B) (C) (D)   70. (A) (B) (C) (D)
47. (A) (B) (C) (D)   71. (A) (B) (C) (D)
48. (A) (B) (C) (D)   72. (A) (B) (C) (D)
49. (A) (B) (C) (D)   73. (A) (B) (C) (D)
50. (A) (B) (C) (D)   74. (A) (B) (C) (D)
51. (A) (B) (C) (D)   75. (A) (B) (C) (D)
52. (A) (B) (C) (D)   76. (A) (B) (C) (D)
53. (A) (B) (C) (D)   77. (A) (B) (C) (D)
54. (A) (B) (C) (D)   78. (A) (B) (C) (D)

Measurement and Geometry

Data Analysis and Probability

55. (A) (B) (C) (D)   79. (A) (B) (C) (D)
56. (A) (B) (C) (D)   80. (A) (B) (C) (D)
57. (A) (B) (C) (D)   81. (A) (B) (C) (D)
58. (A) (B) (C) (D)   82. (A) (B) (C) (D)
59. (A) (B) (C) (D)   83. (A) (B) (C) (D)
60. (A) (B) (C) (D)   84. (A) (B) (C) (D)
61. (A) (B) (C) (D)
62. (A) (B) (C) (D)   ## Problem Solving
63. (A) (B) (C) (D)
64. (A) (B) (C) (D)   85. (A) (B) (C) (D)
65. (A) (B) (C) (D)   86. (A) (B) (C) (D)
66. (A) (B) (C) (D)   87. (A) (B) (C) (D)
67. (A) (B) (C) (D)   88. (A) (B) (C) (D)
68. (A) (B) (C) (D)   89. (A) (B) (C) (D)
69. (A) (B) (C) (D)   90. (A) (B) (C) (D)

Name _____

Answer Key

Mark the space that corresponds to the correct answer.   Form A ___   Form B ✓

Numeration, Patterns, and Relationships

1. (A) (B) (C) (D)
2. (A) (B) (C) (D)
3. (A) (B) (C) (D)
4. (A) (B) (C) (D)
5. (A) (B) (C) (D)
6. (A) (B) (C) (D)
7. (A) (B) (C) (D)
8. (A) (R) (C) (D)
9. (A) (B) (C) (D)
10. (A) (B) (C) (D)
11. (A) (B) (C) (D)

Operations with Whole Numbers

12. (A) (B) (C) (D)
13. (A) (B) (C) (D)
14. (A) (B) (C) (D)
15. (A) (B) (C) (D)
16. (A) (B) (C) (D)
17. (A) (B) (C) (D)
18. (A) (B) (C) (D)
19. (A) (B) (C) (D)
20. (A) (B) (C) (D)
21. (A) (B) (C) (D)
22. (A) (B) (C) (D)

23. (A) (B) (C) (D)
24. (A) (B) (C) (D)
25. (A) (B) (C) (D)
26. (A) (B) (C) (D)
27. (A) (B) (C) (D)
28. (A) (B) (C) (D)
29. (A) (B) (C) (D)
30. (A) (B) (C) (D)
31. (A) (B) (C) (D)
32. (A) (B) (C) (D)

Fractions, Decimals, and Percents

33. (A) (B) (C) (D)
34. (A) (B) (C) (D)
35. (A) (B) (C) (D)
36. (A) (B) (C) (D)
37. (A) (B) (C) (D)
38. (A) (B) (C) (D)
39. (A) (B) (C) (D)
40. (A) (B) (C) (D)
41. (A) (B) (C) (D)
42. (A) (B) (C) (D)
43. (A) (B) (C) (D)
44. (A) (B) (C) (D)
45. (A) (B) (C) (D)

67

Answer Key (continued)

Mark the space that corresponds to the correct answer.   Form A ___   Form B ✓

___

46. (A) (B) (C) **(D)**
47. (A) **(B)** (C) (D)
48. (A) (B) (C) **(D)**
49. **(A)** (B) (C) (D)
50. **(A)** (B) (C) (D)
51. (A) (B) **(C)** (D)
52. **(A)** (B) (C) (D)
53. **(A)** (B) (C) (D)
54. **(A)** (B) (C) (D)

70. (A) (B) **(C)** (D)
71. **(A)** (B) (C) (D)
72. **(A)** (B) (C) (D)
73. (A) (B) **(C)** (D)
74. (A) **(B)** (C) (D)
75. (A) **(B)** (C) (D)
76. (A) (B) (C) **(D)**
77. (A) (B) **(C)** (D)
78. **(A)** (B) (C) (D)

Measurement and Geometry

55. (A) (B) **(C)** (D)
56. (A) (B) **(C)** (D)
57. (A) **(B)** (C) (D)
58. (A) **(B)** (C) (D)
59. (A) (B) **(C)** (D)
60. (A) (B) (C) **(D)**
61. (A) (B) (C) **(D)**
62. (A) **(B)** (C) (D)
63. **(A)** (B) (C) (D)
64. **(A)** (B) (C) (D)
65. (A) (B) (C) **(D)**
66. (A) (B) **(C)** (D)
67. (A) **(B)** (C) (D)
68. (A) (B) **(C)** (D)
69. **(A)** (B) (C) (D)

Data Analysis and Probability

79. (A) (B) **(C)** (D)
80. **(A)** (B) (C) (D)
81. (A) (B) **(C)** (D)
82. **(A)** (B) (C) (D)
83. **(A)** (B) (C) (D)
84. **(A)** (B) (C) (D)

Problem Solving

85. (A) (B) (C) **(D)**
86. (A) (B) **(C)** (D)
87. **(A)** (B) (C) (D)
88. (A) (B) (C) **(D)**
89. (A) (B) **(C)** (D)
90. (A) (B) (C) **(D)**

Name _____

Numeration, Patterns, and Relationships

Read each question. Then mark your answer on the sheet.

---

1. What is the value of the 4 in 5,224,759,600?

   A Four thousand

   B Forty thousand

   C Four hundred thousand

   D Four million

---

2. Which list shows these numbers ordered from greatest to least?

   A 7,890,900; 7,809,900; 5,475,700; 4,979,450

   B 7,809,900; 7,890,900; 5,475,700; 4,979,450

   C 4,979,450; 5,475,700; 7,890,900; 7,809,900

   D 4,979,450; 5,475,700; 7,809,900; 7,890,900

---

3. A company raised $17,517,859 for charity. Rounded to the nearest hundred thousand, how much money was raised?

   A $17,000,000

   B $17,500,000

   C $17,500,900

   D $18,000,000

---

4. Which number shows the location of point *B*?

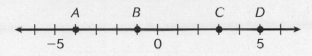

   A −2   C 2

   B −1   D 3

---

5. Which ordered pair names point *A*?

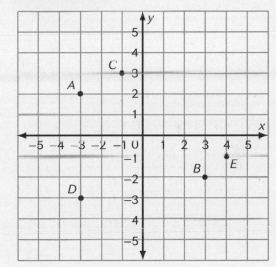

   A (−1, 3)

   B (−3, 2)

   C (3, −2)

   D (2, −3)

---

6. What is the distance between points at (4, 1) and (4, 5)?

   A 5 units   C 3 units

   B 4 units   D 2 units

Read each question. Then mark your answer on the sheet.

7. Which ordered pair is located on line *m*?

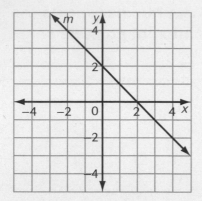

   A $(-1, 3)$

   B $(1, -3)$

   C $(-2, -4)$

   D $(2, 4)$

8. Which equation matches the table?

m	*n*
3	9
6	12
1	7
7	13

   A $n = m + 6$ **C** $n = 2m$

   B $n = m + 5$ **D** $n = 3m$

9. Evaluate $(18 \div 3) \div (9 - 7)$.

   A 1

   B 3

   C 8

   D 12

10. A gallon of milk contains 128 ounces. Which expression shows the number of ounces in *g* gallons?

   A $128 + g$

   B $128 \div g$

   C $128g$

   D $g - 128$

11. If $n = 15$, what is $423 - n$?

   A 438   **C** 293

   B 408   **D** 273

12. Find the value of *n*.

$$\frac{n}{5} = 8$$

   A $n = 40$ **C** $n = 13$

   B $n = 32$ **D** $n = 3$

13. Find the value of *n*.

$7(n + 5) = (7 \times 4) + (7 \times 5)$

   A $n = 3$ **C** $n = 5$

   B $n = 4$ **D** $n = 6$

14. What value of *b* makes the equation true?

$(7 \times 3) \times 4 = 7 \times (b \times 4)$

   A $b = 3$ **C** $b = 7$

   B $b = 4$ **D** $b = 10$

Operations with Whole Numbers

Read each question. Then mark your answer on the sheet.

---

15. What is 17,319 − 892?

A 16,317

B 16,427

C 17,427

D 18,211

---

16. What is 23,519 + 8,615?

A 14,904

B 31,132

C 32,124

D 32,134

---

17. A baker made 1,296 rolls on Monday. He put 6 rolls in each package. How many packages of rolls did the baker make on Monday?

A 21 packages

B 206 packages

C 212 packages

D 216 packages

---

18. Use an exponent to write 3 × 3 × 3 × 3 × 3.

A 3^3

B 3^4

C 3^5

D 5^3

---

19. Which number is prime?

A 22   C 71

B 39   D 111

---

20. Which is the prime factorization of 78?

A 2 × 3 × 13

B 2 × 2 × 3 × 13

C 2 × 2 × 2 × 13

D 2 × 39

---

21. What is the GCF of 12 and 18?

A 2

B 3

C 6

D 9

---

22. Judy buys balloons in packages of 6. She buys colored string for the balloons in packages of 4. What is the smallest number of packages of string she should purchase to be sure she has the same number of balloons and strings?

A 24 packages

B 20 packages

C 12 packages

D 3 packages

Name _____

Operations with Whole Numbers (continued)

Read each question. Then mark your answer on the sheet.

23. Which number is divisible by 2, 3, 6, and 9?

    A 21

    B 84

    C 198

    D 436

24.   340
    × 10

    A 340

    B 350

    C 3,400

    D 34,000

25. Alexa has 45 boxes of baseball cards. Each box has 225 baseball cards. How many cards does Alexa have in all?

    A 9,000 cards

    B 9,905 cards

    C 9,925 cards

    D 10,125 cards

26. 2,700 ÷ 30 =

    A 9

    B 90

    C 900

    D 9,000

27. Mandy has 230 pictures. She wants to place an equal amount of pictures on 12 different posters. About how many pictures should be placed on each poster?

    A About 10 pictures

    B About 15 pictures

    C About 20 pictures

    D About 25 pictures

28. 32)268

    A 8

    B 8 R9

    C 8 R12

    D 8 R16

29. 73)61,324

    A 840 R4

    B 840 R40

    C 841 R14

    D 841 R40

Fractions, Decimals, and Percents

Read each question. Then mark your answer on the sheet.

---

30. Find $5 \div 7$.

  A $1\frac{2}{5}$ **C** $\frac{7}{5}$

  B $1\frac{2}{7}$ **D** $\frac{5}{7}$

---

31. What is the improper fraction $\frac{24}{5}$ written as a mixed number?

  A $4\frac{1}{5}$ **C** $4\frac{4}{5}$

  B $4\frac{3}{5}$ **D** $5\frac{1}{5}$

---

32. Which statement is true?

  A $\frac{1}{2} > \frac{4}{6}$

  B $\frac{2}{3} = \frac{3}{9}$

  C $\frac{3}{6} > \frac{1}{2}$

  D $\frac{3}{8} < \frac{5}{6}$

---

33. Which is $\frac{18}{40}$ in simplest form?

  A $\frac{9}{15}$ **C** $\frac{6}{13}$

  B $\frac{9}{20}$ **D** $\frac{9}{10}$

---

34. Which is three and thirty-one millionths in decimal form?

  A 3.031

  B 3.0031

  C 3.00031

  D 3.000031

---

35. Which is 23.862 rounded to the nearest tenth?

  A 20

  B 23.8

  C 23.86

  D 23.9

---

36. Which is NOT correct?

  A $0.36 < 0.3$

  B $0.6 - 0.60$

  C $0.46 > 0.45$

  D $3.291 > 3.219$

---

37. Which of the following is equal to $\frac{6}{10}$?

  A 0.06   **C** 0.66

  B 0.6   **D** 6.0

---

38. Point P can be represented by which fraction and decimal?

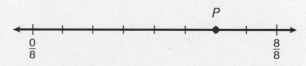

  A $\frac{3}{8}$ and 0.375

  B $\frac{4}{8}$ and 0.5

  C $\frac{5}{8}$ and 0.75

  D $\frac{6}{8}$ and 0.75

Fractions, Decimals, and Percents (continued)

Read each question. Then mark your answer on the sheet.

39. Fisher bought $\frac{2}{3}$ pound of cashews and $\frac{3}{4}$ pound of peanuts for the company picnic. How many pounds of nuts did Fisher buy?

    A $\frac{5}{7}$ pound

    B $1\frac{1}{3}$ pounds

    C $1\frac{1}{4}$ pounds

    D $1\frac{5}{12}$ pounds

40. Janet bought $\frac{7}{8}$ pound of grapes. She used $\frac{3}{4}$ pound in a fruit salad. How much did she have left?

    A $\frac{1}{8}$ pound

    B $\frac{1}{4}$ pound

    C $\frac{5}{6}$ pound

    D $1\frac{5}{8}$ pounds

41. What is $6\frac{1}{9} + 2\frac{2}{3}$?

    A $8\frac{1}{3}$

    B $8\frac{1}{2}$

    C $8\frac{7}{9}$

    D $8\frac{8}{9}$

42. Mrs. O'Neill bought $2\frac{1}{3}$ pounds of chicken. The recipe she is preparing calls for $1\frac{2}{3}$ pounds of chicken. How much chicken will Mrs. O'Neill have left?

    A $\frac{2}{3}$ pound

    B 1 pound

    C $1\frac{1}{3}$ pounds

    D $1\frac{2}{3}$ pounds

43. There are 32 bagels in a basket. One fourth of them are blueberry bagels. How many bagels are blueberry?

    A 4 bagels   C 12 bagels

    B 8 bagels   D 24 bagels

44. What is $\frac{4}{9} \times \frac{1}{3}$?

    A $\frac{2}{3}$ C $\frac{5}{27}$

    B $\frac{2}{9}$ D $\frac{4}{27}$

45. What is $1\frac{1}{2} \times 3\frac{1}{4}$?

    A $4\frac{7}{8}$

    B $4\frac{8}{9}$

    C $5\frac{1}{2}$

    D $5\frac{7}{8}$

Fractions, Decimals, and Percents (continued)

Read each question. Then mark your answer on the sheet.

---

46. A bread recipe calls for 5 cups of flour. If you add flour to the dough $\frac{1}{4}$ cup at a time, how many times will you add flour to the dough?

A $\frac{5}{4}$

B 10

C 15

D 20

---

47. The odometer on a bike showed 38.4 miles at the end of the first day and 52.9 miles at the end of the second day. About how many miles was the bike ridden the second day?

A About 90 miles

B About 53 miles

C About 15 miles

D About 8 miles

---

48. Lenny's fence is 6.9 meters long. He adds a new section that is 2.19 meters long. What is the total length of the fence?

A 4.71 meters

B 9.09 meters

C 9.19 meters

D 9.99 meters

---

49. Kevin finished the race in 43.62 seconds. Melvin finished the race in 51.06 seconds. How much faster did Kevin run the race?

A 7.24 seconds

B 7.34 seconds

C 7.44 seconds

D 8.34 seconds

---

50. Each bottle holds 3.78 liters of grape juice. About how many liters of grape juice would Cher have if she bought 6 bottles?

A About 16 liters

B About 18 liters

C About 20 liters

D About 24 liters

---

51. What is 3.5×0.05?

A 0.0175   **C** 1.75

B 0.175   **D** 17.5

---

52. $24\overline{)2.16}$

A 0.9   **C** 0.18

B 0.8   **D** 0.09

Name _____

Fractions, Decimals, and Percents (continued)

Read each question. Then mark your answer on the sheet.

53. What is 0.343 ÷ 0.07?

A 0.049

B 0.49

C 4.9

D 49

54. What is the ratio of triangles to squares?

A 3:5

B 5:3

C 3:8

D 8:3

55. Which percent names the shaded part?

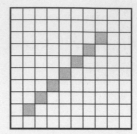

A 40%

B 47%

C 49%

D 51%

56. Which does not represent the shaded part?

A 7%   C $\frac{7}{100}$

B 0.07   D 0.7

57. A survey showed that $\frac{1}{4}$ of the people who saw the latest movie at the theater did not like it. What percent of the people liked the movie?

A 10%   C 75%

B 25%   D 80%

58. Which shows 12% as a fraction in simplest form?

A $\frac{1}{2}$ C $\frac{12}{100}$

B $\frac{3}{25}$ D $\frac{1}{12}$

59. What is 30% of 200?

A 20

B 30

C 40

D 60

Measurement and Geometry

Read each question. Then mark your answer on the sheet.

Use the figure for Questions 60 and 61.

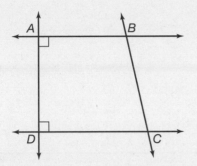

60. Which line is perpendicular to $\overleftrightarrow{AB}$?

A $\overleftrightarrow{AB}$ C $\overleftrightarrow{DC}$

B $\overleftrightarrow{BC}$ D $\overleftrightarrow{AD}$

61. Which line appears to be parallel to $\overleftrightarrow{AB}$?

A $\overleftrightarrow{BC}$

B $\overleftrightarrow{AD}$

C $\overleftrightarrow{DB}$

D $\overleftrightarrow{DC}$

62. Hillary built a triangular sandbox for her sister. Each side was 5 meters long. What type of triangle did she form?

A Equilateral

B Isosceles

C Scalene

D Straight

63. What is the measure of angle A in the quadrilateral?

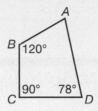

A 62°   C 82°

B 72°   D 102°

Use the figures for Questions 64 and 65.

Figure A   Figure B   Figure C   Figure D

64. Which figure has only one line of symmetry?

A Figure A

B Figure B

C Figure C

D Figure D

65. Which figure can be rotated 180° and fall back on itself?

A Figure A

B Figure B

C Figure C

D Figure D

Measurement and Geometry (continued)

Read each question. Then mark your answer on the sheet.

---

66. **Which solid will the net form?**

- **A** Cube
- **B** Rectangular prism
- **C** Square pyramid
- **D** Triangular pyramid

---

67. **Which is the top view of the figure?**

A   **C**

B   **D**

---

68. **Which is the best estimate for the weight of a volleyball?**

- **A** 1 ounce
- **B** 9 ounces
- **C** 9 pounds
- **D** 90 pounds

---

69. **Fred has 24 quarts of milk. How many 1-gallon containers can he fill?**

- **A** 6
- **B** 12
- **C** 48
- **D** 96

---

70. **7,500 m = _____ km**

- **A** 7.5
- **B** 75
- **C** 750
- **D** 7,500

---

71. **At 7:45 Friday evening Carrie decorates for her party. The party begins at 1:30 Saturday afternoon. How long does Carrie have to wait until her party begins?**

- **A** 17 hours 45 minutes
- **B** 17 hours 15 minutes
- **C** 6 hours 15 minutes
- **D** 5 hours 45 minutes

---

72. **The temperature at noon is 36°F. It was 9°F colder at 8:00 A.M. What was the temperature at 8:00 A.M.?**

- **A** 45°F
- **C** 33°F
- **B** 37°F
- **D** 27°F

Name _____

Math Diagnosis and Intervention System
Grade 5 **Diagnostic Test, Form A**

Measurement and Geometry (continued)

Read each question. Then mark your answer on the sheet.

73. What is the perimeter of the figure?

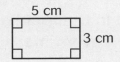

5 cm

3 cm

A 8 cm   **C** 16 cm

B 14 cm   **D** 18 cm

74. Jason's garden is a rectangle 7 meters wide and 8 meters long. He divides the garden by putting a string from one corner diagonally to the opposite corner. He plants corn on one side of the string. What is the area planted in corn?

A 14 square meters

B 28 square meters

C 42 square meters

D 56 square meters

75. Which is the area of the figure shown?

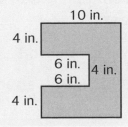

10 in.

4 in.

6 in.   4 in.
6 in.

4 in.

A 96 square inches

B 104 square inches

C 112 square inches

D 120 square inches

76. What is the volume of the figure?

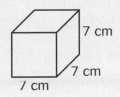

7 cm

7 cm

7 cm

A 343 cm³

B 283 cm³

C 49 cm³

D 21 cm³

77. Meredith needs to wrap a box with paper. The box measures 6 inches wide, 8 inches long, and 9 inches tall. What is the surface area of the box?

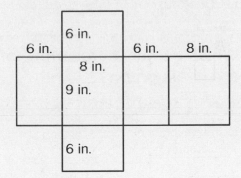

6 in.

6 in.   6 in.   8 in.

8 in.

9 in.

6 in.

A 300 in.²

B 348 in.²

C 432 in.²

D 864 in.²

Data Analysis and Probability

Read each question. Then mark your answer on the sheet.

---

78. How many people reported they needed 35 minutes to solve the crossword puzzle?

Minutes Needed to Solve a Crossword Puzzle

Stem	Leaves
1	9
2	4 4 5 6 9 9
3	0 0 1 1 1 2 4 4 5 5 5 6 8 8 8
4	1 3 7 8
5	2 3

A 3

B 2

C 1

D 0

---

79. Which sector represents $\frac{1}{3}$ of the circle graph?

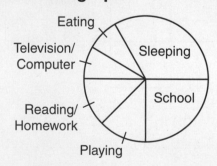

A School

B Sleeping

C Play

D Other

---

80. The line graph shows how the number of computers for each student in U.S. public schools changed over time.

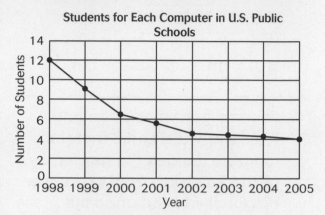

Students for Each Computer in U.S. Public Schools

What was the first year when there were less than 6 students for each computer?

A 2003

B 2002

C 2001

D 2000

---

81. The following represent the scores Janzen made on his math tests.

   88   72   94   89   97

What is his mean score?

A 84

B 86

C 88

D 440

Data Analysis and Probability (continued)

Read each question. Then mark your answer on the sheet.

---

82. Find the median for this set of data.

Boys' Weight (lb)						
98	103	65	89	92	97	89

A 38 lb

B 89 lb

C 90.4 lb

D 92 lb

83. Which group's tour showed the greatest difference between the number of cities visited and the number of shows played?

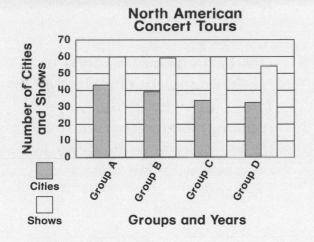

North American
Concert Tours

Cities

Shows

A Group A

B Group B

C Group C

D Group D

84. Bob has two pairs of shorts and 5 shirts. He wears one pair of shorts and one shirt to school. What is the total number of short and shirt combinations he can wear to school?

A 12

B 10

C 7

D 3

85. A bag contains 3 red apples, 7 green apples, and 2 yellow apples. What is the probability of getting a red apple if you reach in and take one without looking?

A $\frac{1}{6}$ C $\frac{1}{3}$

B $\frac{1}{4}$ D $\frac{7}{10}$

86. What is the probability that a T-shirt will be sold next?

Souvenir Shop	
Item	Number Sold
Postcard	7
Toy	10
T-shirt	8

A $\frac{8}{25}$

B $\frac{8}{17}$

C $\frac{7}{25}$

D $\frac{2}{25}$

Problem Solving

Read each question. Then mark your answer on the sheet.

---

87. How much more will it cost Heather to buy 24 tulips rather than 24 marigolds?

Dave's Garden Center	
Tulips	$0.33 each
Daisies	$0.75 each
Roses	$9.00 each
Marigolds	$0.25 each

A $7.92   C $2.29

B $6.00   D $1.92

---

88. In a group of children, there are 5 boys for every 6 girls. How many boys are there in the group if there are 48 girls?

Boys	5	10						
Girls	6	12	18					

A 30 boys

B 40 boys

C 50 boys

D 60 boys

---

89. There are 24 servings in a box of 144 crackers. Which equation can be used to find how many crackers are in each serving?

A $144 + 24 = n$

B $144 - 24 = n$

C $24 \times 144 = n$

D $144 \div 24 = n$

---

90. Suppose the stack of cubes shown is painted so that the top and bottom of the stack are green and the other 4 faces of the stack are yellow. How many of the cubes have both green and yellow faces?

A 12 cubes

B 10 cubes

C 8 cubes

D 4 cubes

---

91. One large dish of lasagna calls for 24 ounces of cheese. Which of the following is the only reasonable number of large dishes of lasagna that can be made with 216 ounces of cheese?

A 4 dishes

B 9 dishes

C 12 dishes

D 20 dishes

Numeration, Patterns, and Relationships

Read each question. Then mark your answer on the sheet.

1. **What is the value of the 6 in the number 4,526,332,871?**

   A 6 billion

   B 600 thousand

   C 6 hundred thousand

   D 6 million

2. **Which list shows these numbers ordered from least to greatest?**

   A 5,687,423; 5,867,423;
      6,587,423; 6,857,423

   B 5,867,423; 5,687,423;
      6,587,423; 6,857,423

   C 6,857,423; 5,687,423;
      5,867,423; 6,587,423

   D 6,587,423; 6,857,423;
      5,687,423; 5,867,423

3. **A company manufactured 2,487,200 trinkets last year. What is the number of trinkets they made rounded to the nearest hundred thousand?**

   A 2,500,000

   B 2,490,000

   C 2,400,000

   D 2,000,000

4. **Which number shows the location of point *B*?**

   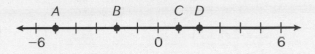

   A −3   C −1

   B −2   D 2

5. **Which ordered pair names point *A*?**

   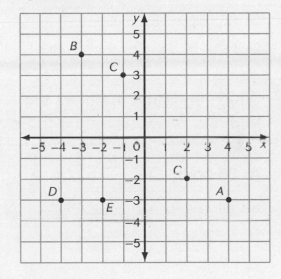

   A (−4, −3)

   B (4, −3)

   C (−3, 4)

   D (−2, −3)

6. **What is the distance between points at (2, 3) and (5, 3)?**

   A 4 units   C 2 units

   B 3 units   D 1 unit

Numeration, Patterns, and Relationships (continued)

Read each question. Then mark your answer on the sheet.

---

7. Which ordered pair is located on line *m*?

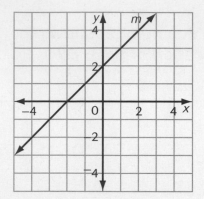

   A $(-3, -1)$

   B $(-1, -3)$

   C $(2, -4)$

   D $(-4, 2)$

---

8. Which equation matches the table?

m	n
5	20
8	32
4	16
6	24

   A $n = 4m$ **C** $n = m + 15$

   B $n = 5m$ **D** $n = m + 12$

---

9. Evaluate $(24 \div 6) \times (3 + 2)$.

   A 20

   B 15

   C 14

   D 12

---

10. Steven walked up 6 steps, then he walked up some more steps. Which expression shows the number of steps Steven walked?

   A $6 \div x$

   B $6x$

   C $x - 6$

   D $6 + x$

---

11. If $n = 13$, what is $302 - n$?

   A 269   **C** 289

   B 279   **D** 299

---

12. Find the value of *n*.

$$\frac{n}{9} = 5$$

   A $n = 4$ **C** $n = 45$

   B $n = 14$ **D** $n = 54$

---

13. Find the value of *n*.

$8(3 + 5) = (8 \times 3) + (8 \times n)$

   A $n = 3$ **C** $n = 8$

   B $n = 5$ **D** $n = 40$

---

14. What value of *c* makes the equation true?

$(8 \times 2) \times 5 = (2 \times c) \times 5$

   A $c = 8$ **C** $c = 5$

   B $c = 6$ **D** $c = 2$

Operations with Whole Numbers

Read each question. Then mark your answer on the sheet.

15. What is 56,982 − 11,891?

   A 68,873

   B 45,111

   C 45,091

   D 44,181

16. What is 39,612 + 13,468?

   A 26,144

   B 52,180

   C 53,070

   D 53,080

17. The library bought 2,346 books. The books will be sent in 3 equal shipments. How many books will be in each shipment?

   A 882 books

   B 802 books

   C 792 books

   D 782 books

18. Use an exponent to write 7 × 7 × 7 × 7.

   A 7^4

   B 7^5

   C 7^7

   D 4^7

19. Which number is not prime?

   A 7

   B 31

   C 39

   D 59

20. Which is the prime factorization of 63?

   A $2^3 \times 7$

   B $3^2 \times 7$

   C $3^3 \times 7$

   D 7×9

21. What is the GCF of 45 and 90?

   A 5

   B 10

   C 15

   D 45

22. Sheila records the outdoor temperature every 3 hours. She records the wind rate every 5 hours. If she just recorded both the temperature and the wind rate, in how many hours will she again record both the temperature and the wind rate?

   A 5 hours   **C** 15 hours

   B 10 hours   **D** 30 hours

Operations with Whole Numbers (continued)

Read each question. Then mark your answer on the sheet.

23. Which number is divisible by 2, 3, 4, and 9?

    A 479

    B 843

    C 3,459

    D 6,156

24. $\begin{array}{r} 810 \\ \times\, 100 \\ \hline \end{array}$

    A 810

    B 8,100

    C 81,000

    D 810,000

25. Each section of the arena seats 876 people. The arena has 22 sections. How many people can sit in the arena?

    A 19,272 people

    B 19,062 people

    C 18,062 people

    D 3,504 people

26. 56,000 ÷ 800 =

    A 7

    B 70

    C 700

    D 7,000

27. Tandy has 207 stamps. She needs to put 30 stamps in each envelope. About how many envelopes will she need?

    A About 7 envelopes

    B About 8 envelopes

    C About 10 envelopes

    D About 70 envelopes

28. $72\overline{)318}$

    A 3 R30

    B 4 R22

    C 4 R30

    D 5 R30

29. $22\overline{)18,924}$

    A 850 R4

    B 859 R4

    C 860 R4

    D 860 R40

86

Fractions, Decimals, and Percents

Read each question. Then mark your answer on the sheet.

---

30. Find 3 ÷ 10.

  A $\frac{3}{10}$ **C** $3\frac{1}{10}$

  B $\frac{1}{3}$ **D** $3\frac{1}{3}$

---

31. What is the improper fraction $\frac{61}{7}$ written as a mixed number?

  A $7\frac{2}{7}$ **C** $8\frac{4}{7}$

  B $8\frac{2}{7}$ **D** $8\frac{5}{7}$

---

32. Which statement is true?

  A $\frac{4}{6} = \frac{1}{3}$

  B $\frac{8}{10} > \frac{5}{5}$

  C $\frac{3}{10} < \frac{1}{2}$

  D $\frac{1}{7} > \frac{7}{14}$

---

33. Which is $\frac{15}{25}$ in simplest form?

  A $\frac{3}{5}$ **C** $\frac{2}{7}$

  B $\frac{2}{5}$ **D** $\frac{1}{5}$

---

34. Which is four hundred twelve millionths in decimal form?

  A 0.000412

  B 0.00412

  C 0.0412

  D 0.412

---

35. Which is 65.239 rounded to the nearest hundredth?

  A 65.0

  B 65.2

  C 65.23

  D 65.24

---

36. Which is NOT correct?

  A 0.02 < 0.2

  B 0.10 = 0.1

  C 0.86 < 0.85

  D 3.625 > 3.265

---

37. Which of the following is equal to $\frac{2}{10}$?

  A 0.2   **C** 0.4

  B 0.3   **D** 0.5

---

38. Point *P* can be represented by which fraction and decimal?

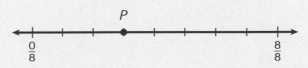

  A $\frac{3}{8}$ and 0.375

  B $\frac{4}{8}$ and 0.5

  C $\frac{5}{8}$ and 0.75

  D $\frac{6}{8}$ and 0.75

Fractions, Decimals, and Percents (continued)

Read each question. Then mark your answer on the sheet.

39. Eddie studied for $\frac{1}{3}$ hour on Monday and $\frac{1}{4}$ hour on Tuesday. How long did he study in all?

   A $\frac{1}{4}$ hour

   B $\frac{1}{2}$ hour

   C $\frac{7}{12}$ hour

   D $\frac{2}{3}$ hour

40. Oscar ran $\frac{5}{8}$ mile. Tony ran $\frac{5}{6}$ mile. How much farther did Tony run?

   A $\frac{5}{24}$ mile

   B $\frac{1}{3}$ mile

   C $\frac{7}{8}$ mile

   D $1\frac{11}{24}$ miles

41. What is $2\frac{5}{8} + 3\frac{1}{6}$?

   A $5\frac{3}{8}$

   B $5\frac{17}{24}$

   C $5\frac{3}{4}$

   D $5\frac{19}{24}$

42. Mrs. Myers bought $6\frac{3}{8}$ yards of ribbon. She used $5\frac{7}{8}$ yards of ribbon on her daughter's dress. How much ribbon did she have left?

   A $\frac{1}{2}$ yard

   B $1\frac{1}{8}$ yards

   C $1\frac{1}{2}$ yards

   D $1\frac{3}{4}$ yards

43. There are 25 marbles in a bag. Two fifths of them are red. How many marbles are red?

   A 5 marbles

   B 10 marbles

   C 15 marbles

   D 20 marbles

44. What is $\frac{3}{8} \times \frac{2}{5}$?

   A $\frac{1}{8}$ C $\frac{5}{13}$

   B $\frac{3}{20}$ D $\frac{25}{40}$

45. What is $2\frac{5}{6} \times 1\frac{1}{2}$?

   A $2\frac{5}{12}$ C $4\frac{1}{4}$

   B $4\frac{1}{12}$ D $4\frac{1}{2}$

Fractions, Decimals, and Percents (continued)

Read each question. Then mark your answer on the sheet.

46. Kendra has 16 pints of blueberries. If she wants to divide them into half pints, how many will she have?

   A 4 half pints

   B 8 half pints

   C 32 half pints

   D 42 half pints

47. You have a spool of ribbon containing 16.25 feet and a spool containing 7.375 feet. About how much ribbon do you have all together?

   A About 8 feet

   B About 9 feet

   C About 20 feet

   D About 23 feet

48. Sam was 50.75 centimeters tall when he was born. Over the next two years he grew 25.5 centimeters. How tall was he then?

   A 25.25 centimeters

   B 53.3 centimeters

   C 75.25 centimeters

   D 76.25 centimeters

49. Ashley rode a total of 34.75 miles. Megan rode a total of 36.20 miles. How many more miles did Megan ride?

   A 1.45 miles

   B 1.55 miles

   C 2.35 miles

   D 70.95 miles

50. Marcus drives a total of 87.64 miles to and from school each week. About how many miles does he drive in 8 weeks?

   A About 900 miles

   B About 720 miles

   C About 700 miles

   D About 640 miles

51. What is 0.014×2.3?

   A 3.22   C 0.0322

   B 0.322   D 0.00322

52. $6\overline{)98.4}$

   A 1.64   C 16.4

   B 15.9   D 16.6

Fractions, Decimals, and Percents (continued)

Read each question. Then mark your answer on the sheet.

___

53. What is 28.8 ÷ 0.9?

A 0.032

B 0.32

C 3.2

D 32

___

54. What is the ratio of stars to circles?

A 2:5

B 2:7

C 5:2

D 5:7

___

55. Which percent names the shaded part?

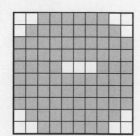

A 15%

B 75%

C 85%

D 90%

___

56. Which does not represent the shaded part?

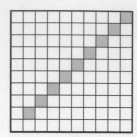

A 0.9   C 0.09

B 9%   D $\frac{9}{100}$

___

57. Sheila has tried 9 out of the 50 flavors of yogurt at Jem's Yogurt Shop. What is the percent of the yogurt flavors she has tried?

A 9%

B 15%

C 18%

D 20%

___

58. Which shows 80% as a fraction in simplest form?

A $\frac{4}{25}$ C $\frac{4}{5}$

B $\frac{8}{25}$ D $\frac{80}{100}$

___

59. What is 25% of 80?

A 4

B 16

C 20

D 36

Measurement and Geometry

Read each question. Then mark your answer on the sheet.

Use the figure for Questions 60 and 61.

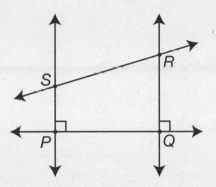

60. Name a line perpendicular to $\overleftrightarrow{RQ}$.

A $\overleftrightarrow{SR}$ C $\overleftrightarrow{PQ}$

B $\overleftrightarrow{SP}$ D $\overleftrightarrow{QR}$

61. Which line is parallel to $\overleftrightarrow{RQ}$?

A $\overleftrightarrow{PQ}$

B $\overleftrightarrow{SP}$

C $\overleftrightarrow{SR}$

D $\overleftrightarrow{QR}$

62. Martin made a triangular flower bed. One side was 14 feet, a second side was 6 feet, and the third side was 10 feet. What type of triangle did Martin form?

A Equilateral

B Isosceles

C Scalene

D Straight

63. What is the measure of angle *A* in the quadrilateral?

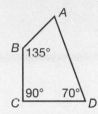

A 65°   C 85°

B 75°   D 110°

Use the figures for Questions 64 and 65.

Figure A   Figure B   Figure C   Figure D

64. Which figure has more than one line of symmetry?

A Figure A

B Figure B

C Figure C

D Figure D

65. Which figure can be rotated 90° and fall back on itself?

A Figure A

B Figure B

C Figure C

D Figure D

Measurement and Geometry (continued)

Read each question. Then mark your answer on the sheet.

---

66. **Which solid will the net form?**

- **A** Cylinder
- **B** Cone
- **C** Square pyramid
- **D** Sphere

---

67. **Which is the top view of the figure?**

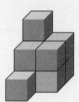

A   **C**

B   **D**

---

68. **Which is the best estimate for the weight of a watermelon?**

- **A** 8 ounces
- **B** 8 pounds
- **C** 80 pounds
- **D** 800 pounds

---

69. **Brittany bought 5 gallons of distilled water. How many quarts is that?**

- **A** 40 quarts
- **B** 20 quarts
- **C** 10 quarts
- **D** 1.25 quarts

---

70. **97 mm = _____ cm**

- **A** 9,700
- **B** 970
- **C** 9.7
- **D** 0.97

---

71. **Todd's recital is at 3:30 Saturday afternoon. It is currently 8:45 the Friday evening before. How long does Todd have to wait for his recital?**

- **A** 18 hours 45 minutes
- **B** 18 hours 15 minutes
- **C** 6 hours 45 minutes
- **D** 5 hours 15 minutes

---

72. **The temperature at 4:00 P.M. was 72°F. At noon, it was 8°F colder. What was the temperature at noon?**

- **A** 64°F   **C** 78°F
- **B** 66°F   **D** 80°F

Measurement and Geometry (continued)

Read each question. Then mark your answer on the sheet.

---

73. What is the perimeter of the figure?

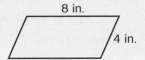

A 16 in. **C** 28 in.

B 24 in. **D** 32 in.

---

74. Mark shares a room with his brother. The room is a rectangle 10 feet wide and 15 feet long. Mark divides the room along a diagonal from one corner to the opposite corner. What is the area of Mark's part of the room?

A 150 square feet

B 100 square feet

C 75 square feet

D 60 square feet

---

75. Celia is buying new carpet for the room shown. How much carpet does she need?

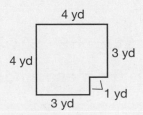

A 15 square yards

B 16 square yards

C 17 square yards

D 18 square yards

---

76. What is the volume of the figure?

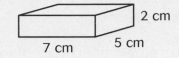

A 70 cm³
70 cm^3

B 55 cm³
55 cm^3

C 35 cm³
35 cm^3

D 14 cm³
14 cm^3

---

77. Courtney needs to wrap a gift that is in a box that measures 4 inches wide, 6 inches long, and 3 inches tall. What is the surface area of the box?

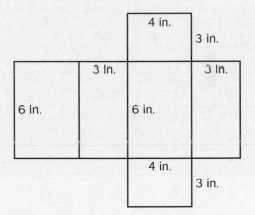

A 72 in.^2

B 108 in.^2

C 120 in.^2

D 144 in.^2

Data Analysis and Probability

Read each question. Then mark your answer on the sheet.

---

78. How many people solved the crossword puzzle in less than 30 minutes?

**Minutes Needed to Solve a
Crossword Puzzle**

Stem	Leaves
1	9
2	4 4 5 6 9 9
3	0 0 1 1 1 2 4 4 5 5 5 6 8 8 8
4	1 3 7 8
5	2 3

A 7

B 6

C 2

D 1

---

79. Which sector represents $\frac{1}{4}$ of the circle graph?

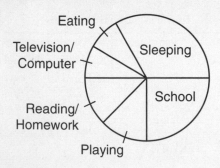

A Reading/homework

B Sleeping

C Television/computer

D School

---

80. The line graph shows how the number of computers for each student in U.S. public schools changed over time.

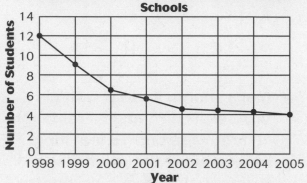

What was the first year when there were less than 8 students for each computer?

A 2003

B 2002

C 2001

D 2000

---

81. The following represents the amounts Leza earned mowing lawns.

$23 $17 $18 $24 $28

What is the mean amount?

A $20

B $22

C $25

D $110

Data Analysis and Probability (continued)

Read each question. Then mark your answer on the sheet.

82. Find the median for this set of data.

Test Scores						
92	86	72	65	83	75	86

A 27

B 80

C 83

D 86

83. Which group's tour showed the least difference between the number of cities visited and the number of shows played?

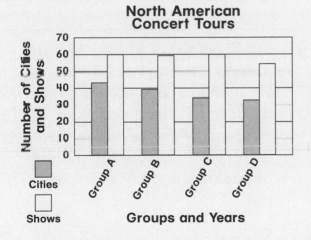

North American
Concert Tours

A Group A

B Group B

C Group C

D Group D

84. Janet has five pairs of earrings and 3 necklaces that she can wear to the school dance. What is the total number of combinations of a pair of earrings and a necklace that she can choose to wear?

A 15   C 5

B 8   D 3

85. A bag contains 2 red marbles, 5 blue marbles, and 3 orange marbles. What is the probability of getting a red marble if you reach in and take one without looking?

A $\frac{1}{5}$ C $\frac{3}{10}$

B $\frac{1}{4}$ D $\frac{1}{2}$

86. What is the probability that a pretzel will be sold?

Concession Sales	
Item	Number Sold
Pretzel	35
Hamburger	10
Veggie Pizza	5

A $\frac{1}{10}$

B $\frac{1}{5}$

C $\frac{1}{2}$

D $\frac{7}{10}$

Problem Solving

Read each question. Then mark your answer on the sheet.

---

87. How much more will it cost to buy 3 pounds of salami than 3 pounds of ham?

Derek's Deli	
Ham	$2.99 per lb
Turkey	$3.19 per lb
Salami	$3.89 per lb

A $0.90   C $2.70

B $1.80   D $5.40

---

88. Each pound of snack mix uses 2 ounces of peanuts, 5 ounces of raisins, and some other nuts. A batch of mix has 12 ounces of peanuts. How many ounces of raisins does this batch of snack mix have?

Peanuts	2	4	6			
Raisins	5	10				

A 30 oz.   C 22 oz.

B 24 oz.   D 19 oz.

---

89. A group of 126 people need to be transported by minibuses. Each minibus holds 18 people. Which can be used to find how many minibuses are needed?

A $126 \div 18 = m$

B $18 \times 126 = m$

C $126 - 18 = m$

D $126 + 18 = m$

---

90. Your mom ordered a quarter-sheet cake for your birthday. The top and sides of the cake are decorated with your favorite frosting. Aunt Debbie would like a piece with as little frosting as possible. How many pieces have only one surface frosted?

A 12 pieces

B 8 pieces

C 5 pieces

D 3 pieces

---

91. Mr. Stykes has 214 stickers to give to his class of 26 students. He plans to give the same number of stickers to each student. Which of the following is the only reasonable number of stickers each student will get?

A 12 stickers

B 10 stickers

C 8 stickers

D 4 stickers

Answer Sheet

Mark the space that corresponds to the correct answer.   Form A ___ Form B ___

Numeration, Patterns, and Relationships

1. (A) (B) (C) (D)
2. (A) (B) (C) (D)
3. (A) (B) (C) (D)
4. (A) (B) (C) (D)
5. (A) (B) (C) (D)
6. (A) (B) (C) (D)
7. (A) (B) (C) (D)
8. (A) (B) (C) (D)
9. (A) (B) (C) (D)
10. (A) (B) (C) (D)
11. (A) (B) (C) (D)
12. (A) (B) (C) (D)
13. (A) (B) (C) (D)
14. (A) (B) (C) (D)

Operations with Whole Numbers

15. (A) (B) (C) (D)
16. (A) (B) (C) (D)
17. (A) (B) (C) (D)
18. (A) (B) (C) (D)
19. (A) (B) (C) (D)
20. (A) (B) (C) (D)
21. (A) (B) (C) (D)
22. (A) (B) (C) (D)

23. (A) (B) (C) (D)
24. (A) (B) (C) (D)
25. (A) (B) (C) (D)
26. (A) (B) (C) (D)
27. (A) (B) (C) (D)
28. (A) (B) (C) (D)
29. (A) (B) (C) (D)

Fractions, Decimals, and Percents

30. (A) (B) (C) (D)
31. (A) (B) (C) (D)
32. (A) (B) (C) (D)
33. (A) (B) (C) (D)
34. (A) (B) (C) (D)
35. (A) (B) (C) (D)
36. (A) (B) (C) (D)
37. (A) (B) (C) (D)
38. (A) (B) (C) (D)
39. (A) (B) (C) (D)
40. (A) (B) (C) (D)
41. (A) (B) (C) (D)
42. (A) (B) (C) (D)
43. (A) (B) (C) (D)
44. (A) (B) (C) (D)
45. (A) (B) (C) (D)

Answer Sheet (continued)

Mark the space that corresponds to the correct answer.   Form A ___ Form B ___

46. Ⓐ Ⓑ Ⓒ Ⓓ   70. Ⓐ Ⓑ Ⓒ Ⓓ

47. Ⓐ Ⓑ Ⓒ Ⓓ   71. Ⓐ Ⓑ Ⓒ Ⓓ

48. Ⓐ Ⓑ Ⓒ Ⓓ   72. Ⓐ Ⓑ Ⓒ Ⓓ

49. Ⓐ Ⓑ Ⓒ Ⓓ   73. Ⓐ Ⓑ Ⓒ Ⓓ

50. Ⓐ Ⓑ Ⓒ Ⓓ   74. Ⓐ Ⓑ Ⓒ Ⓓ

51. Ⓐ Ⓑ Ⓒ Ⓓ   75. Ⓐ Ⓑ Ⓒ Ⓓ

52. Ⓐ Ⓑ Ⓒ Ⓓ   76. Ⓐ Ⓑ Ⓒ Ⓓ

53. Ⓐ Ⓑ Ⓒ Ⓓ   77. Ⓐ Ⓑ Ⓒ Ⓓ

54. Ⓐ Ⓑ Ⓒ Ⓓ

55. Ⓐ Ⓑ Ⓒ Ⓓ   **Data Analysis and Probability**

56. Ⓐ Ⓑ Ⓒ Ⓓ   78. Ⓐ Ⓑ Ⓒ Ⓓ

57. Ⓐ Ⓑ Ⓒ Ⓓ   79. Ⓐ Ⓑ Ⓒ Ⓓ

58. Ⓐ Ⓑ Ⓒ Ⓓ   80. Ⓐ Ⓑ Ⓒ Ⓓ

59. Ⓐ Ⓑ Ⓒ Ⓓ   81. Ⓐ Ⓑ Ⓒ Ⓓ

                              82. Ⓐ Ⓑ Ⓒ Ⓓ

Measurement and Geometry   83. Ⓐ Ⓑ Ⓒ Ⓓ

60. Ⓐ Ⓑ Ⓒ Ⓓ   84. Ⓐ Ⓑ Ⓒ Ⓓ

61. Ⓐ Ⓑ Ⓒ Ⓓ   85. Ⓐ Ⓑ Ⓒ Ⓓ

62. Ⓐ Ⓑ Ⓒ Ⓓ   86. Ⓐ Ⓑ Ⓒ Ⓓ

63. Ⓐ Ⓑ Ⓒ Ⓓ

64. Ⓐ Ⓑ Ⓒ Ⓓ   **Problem Solving**

65. Ⓐ Ⓑ Ⓒ Ⓓ   87. Ⓐ Ⓑ Ⓒ Ⓓ

66. Ⓐ Ⓑ Ⓒ Ⓓ   88. Ⓐ Ⓑ Ⓒ Ⓓ

67. Ⓐ Ⓑ Ⓒ Ⓓ   89. Ⓐ Ⓑ Ⓒ Ⓓ

68. Ⓐ Ⓑ Ⓒ Ⓓ   90. Ⓐ Ⓑ Ⓒ Ⓓ

69. Ⓐ Ⓑ Ⓒ Ⓓ   91. Ⓐ Ⓑ Ⓒ Ⓓ

Name _____

Answer Key

Mark the space that corresponds to the correct answer.   Form A ✔ Form B ___

Numeration, Patterns, and Relationships

1. A B C **D**
2. **A** B C D
3. A **B** C D
4. A **B** C D
5. A **B** C D
6. A **B** C D
7. **A** B C D
8. **A** B C D
9. A **B** C D
10. A B **C** D
11. A **B** C D
12. **A** B C D
13. A **B** C D
14. **A** B C D

Operations with Whole Numbers

15. A **B** C D
16. A B C **D**
17. A B C **D**
18. A B **C** D
19. A B **C** D
20. **A** B C D
21. A B **C** D
22. A B C **D**

23. A B **C** D
24. A B **C** D
25. A B C **D**
26. A **B** C D
27. A B **C** D
28. A B **C** D
29. **A** B C D

Fractions, Decimals, and Percents

30. A B C **D**
31. A B **C** D
32. A B C **D**
33. A **B** C D
34. A B C **D**
35. A B C **D**
36. **A** B C D
37. A **B** C D
38. A B C **D**
39. A B C **D**
40. **A** B C D
41. A B **C** D
42. **A** B C D
43. A **B** C D
44. A B C **D**
45. **A** B C D

Answer Key (continued)

Mark the space that corresponds to the correct answer.   Form A ✓ Form B ___

46. A B C **D**
47. A B **C** D
48. A **B** C D
49. A B **C** D
50. A B C **D**
51. A **B** C D
52. A B C **D**
53. A B **C** D
54. **A** B C D
55. A B **C** D
56. A B C **D**
57. A B **C** D
58. A **B** C D
59. A B C **D**

Measurement and Geometry

60. A B C **D**
61. A B C **D**
62. **A** B C D
63. A **B** C D
64. **A** B C D
65. A **B** C D
66. A B C **D**
67. **A** B C D
68. A **B** C D
69. **A** B C D

70. **A** B C D
71. **A** B C D
72. A B C **D**
73. A B **C** D
74. A **B** C D
75. **A** B C D
76. **A** B C D
77. A **B** C D

Data Analysis and Probability

78. **A** B C D
79. A **B** C D
80. A B **C** D
81. A B **C** D
82. A B C **D**
83. A B **C** D
84. A **B** C D
85. A **B** C D
86. **A** B C D

Problem Solving

87. A B C **D**
88. A **B** C D
89. A B C **D**
90. A B **C** D
91. A **B** C D

Name _____

Answer Key

Mark the space that corresponds to the correct answer.   Form A ___   Form B ✓

Numeration, Patterns, and Relationships

1. Ⓐ Ⓑ Ⓒ **Ⓓ**
2. **Ⓐ** Ⓑ Ⓒ Ⓓ
3. **Ⓐ** Ⓑ Ⓒ Ⓓ
4. Ⓐ **Ⓑ** Ⓒ Ⓓ
5. Ⓐ **Ⓑ** Ⓒ Ⓓ
6. Ⓐ **Ⓑ** Ⓒ Ⓓ
7. **Ⓐ** Ⓑ Ⓒ Ⓓ
8. **Ⓐ** Ⓑ Ⓒ Ⓓ
9. **Ⓐ** Ⓑ Ⓒ Ⓓ
10. Ⓐ Ⓑ Ⓒ **Ⓓ**
11. Ⓐ Ⓑ **Ⓒ** Ⓓ
12. Ⓐ Ⓑ **Ⓒ** Ⓓ
13. Ⓐ **Ⓑ** Ⓒ Ⓓ
14. **Ⓐ** Ⓑ Ⓒ Ⓓ

Operations with Whole Numbers

15. Ⓐ Ⓑ **Ⓒ** Ⓓ
16. Ⓐ Ⓑ Ⓒ **Ⓓ**
17. Ⓐ Ⓑ Ⓒ **Ⓓ**
18. **Ⓐ** Ⓑ Ⓒ Ⓓ
19. Ⓐ Ⓑ **Ⓒ** Ⓓ
20. Ⓐ **Ⓑ** Ⓒ Ⓓ
21. Ⓐ Ⓑ Ⓒ **Ⓓ**
22. Ⓐ Ⓑ **Ⓒ** Ⓓ

23. Ⓐ Ⓑ Ⓒ **Ⓓ**
24. Ⓐ Ⓑ **Ⓒ** Ⓓ
25. **Ⓐ** Ⓑ Ⓒ Ⓓ
26. Ⓐ **Ⓑ** Ⓒ Ⓓ
27. **Ⓐ** Ⓑ Ⓒ Ⓓ
28. Ⓐ Ⓑ **Ⓒ** Ⓓ
29. Ⓐ Ⓑ **Ⓒ** Ⓓ

Fractions, Decimals, and Percents

30. **Ⓐ** Ⓑ Ⓒ Ⓓ
31. Ⓐ Ⓑ Ⓒ **Ⓓ**
32. Ⓐ Ⓑ **Ⓒ** Ⓓ
33. **Ⓐ** Ⓑ Ⓒ Ⓓ
34. **Ⓐ** Ⓑ Ⓒ Ⓓ
35. Ⓐ Ⓑ Ⓒ **Ⓓ**
36. Ⓐ Ⓑ **Ⓒ** Ⓓ
37. **Ⓐ** Ⓑ Ⓒ Ⓓ
38. **Ⓐ** Ⓑ Ⓒ Ⓓ
39. Ⓐ Ⓑ **Ⓒ** Ⓓ
40. **Ⓐ** Ⓑ Ⓒ Ⓓ
41. Ⓐ Ⓑ Ⓒ **Ⓓ**
42. **Ⓐ** Ⓑ Ⓒ Ⓓ
43. Ⓐ **Ⓑ** Ⓒ Ⓓ
44. Ⓐ **Ⓑ** Ⓒ Ⓓ
45. Ⓐ Ⓑ **Ⓒ** Ⓓ

Answer Key (continued)

Mark the space that corresponds to the correct answer.   Form A ___   Form B ✓

46. Ⓐ   Ⓑ   **Ⓒ**   Ⓓ   70. Ⓐ   Ⓑ   **Ⓒ**   Ⓓ

47. Ⓐ   Ⓑ   Ⓒ   **Ⓓ**   71. **Ⓐ**   Ⓑ   Ⓒ   Ⓓ

48. Ⓐ   Ⓑ   Ⓒ   **Ⓓ**   72. **Ⓐ**   Ⓑ   Ⓒ   Ⓓ

49. **Ⓐ**   Ⓑ   Ⓒ   Ⓓ   73. Ⓐ   **Ⓑ**   Ⓒ   Ⓓ

50. Ⓐ   **Ⓑ**   Ⓒ   Ⓓ   74. Ⓐ   Ⓑ   **Ⓒ**   Ⓓ

51. Ⓐ   Ⓑ   **Ⓒ**   Ⓓ   75. **Ⓐ**   Ⓑ   Ⓒ   Ⓓ

52. Ⓐ   Ⓑ   **Ⓒ**   Ⓓ   76. **Ⓐ**   Ⓑ   Ⓒ   Ⓓ

53. Ⓐ   Ⓑ   Ⓒ   **Ⓓ**   77. Ⓐ   **Ⓑ**   Ⓒ   Ⓓ

54. Ⓐ   Ⓑ   **Ⓒ**   Ⓓ

55. Ⓐ   Ⓑ   **Ⓒ**   Ⓓ   ## Data Analysis and Probability

56. **Ⓐ**   Ⓑ   Ⓒ   Ⓓ   78. **Ⓐ**   Ⓑ   Ⓒ   Ⓓ

57. Ⓐ   Ⓑ   **Ⓒ**   Ⓓ   79. Ⓐ   Ⓑ   Ⓒ   **Ⓓ**

58. Ⓐ   Ⓑ   **Ⓒ**   Ⓓ   80. Ⓐ   Ⓑ   Ⓒ   **Ⓓ**

59. Ⓐ   Ⓑ   **Ⓒ**   Ⓓ   81. Ⓐ   **Ⓑ**   Ⓒ   Ⓓ

82. Ⓐ   Ⓑ   **Ⓒ**   Ⓓ

Measurement and Geometry   83. **Ⓐ**   Ⓑ   Ⓒ   Ⓓ

60. Ⓐ   Ⓑ   **Ⓒ**   Ⓓ   84. **Ⓐ**   Ⓑ   Ⓒ   Ⓓ

61. Ⓐ   **Ⓑ**   Ⓒ   Ⓓ   85. **Ⓐ**   Ⓑ   Ⓒ   Ⓓ

62. Ⓐ   Ⓑ   **Ⓒ**   Ⓓ   86. Ⓐ   Ⓑ   Ⓒ   **Ⓓ**

63. **Ⓐ**   Ⓑ   Ⓒ   Ⓓ

64. **Ⓐ**   Ⓑ   Ⓒ   Ⓓ   ## Problem Solving

65. **Ⓐ**   Ⓑ   Ⓒ   Ⓓ   87. Ⓐ   Ⓑ   **Ⓒ**   Ⓓ

66. Ⓐ   **Ⓑ**   Ⓒ   Ⓓ   88. **Ⓐ**   Ⓑ   Ⓒ   Ⓓ

67. **Ⓐ**   Ⓑ   Ⓒ   Ⓓ   89. **Ⓐ**   Ⓑ   Ⓒ   Ⓓ

68. Ⓐ   **Ⓑ**   Ⓒ   Ⓓ   90. Ⓐ   Ⓑ   Ⓒ   **Ⓓ**

69. Ⓐ   **Ⓑ**   Ⓒ   Ⓓ   91. Ⓐ   Ⓑ   **Ⓒ**   Ⓓ

Numeration, Patterns, and Relationships

Read each question. Then mark your answer on the sheet.

1. What is $(4 \times 10^{10}) + (7 \times 10^8)$ in standard form?

   A 47,000,000,000

   B 40,700,000,000

   C 4,700,000,000

   D 4,070,000,000

2. Which submarine is closest to the surface?

Submarine	Depth
Yellow	−30 ft
Green	−60 ft
Blue	−50 ft
Red	−40 ft

   A Yellow

   B Green

   C Blue

   D Red

3. Of the numbers $-\frac{3}{8}$, $\frac{4}{7}$, 0.3, and 0.5, which is farthest to the right on a number line?

   A $-\frac{3}{8}$

   B $\frac{4}{7}$

   C 0.3

   D 0.5

4. What is $-2 + (-9)$?

   A −11   C 7

   B −7   D 11

5. Campsite A is at an altitude of −25 ft. Campsite B is at an altitude of −42 ft. How much higher is Campsite A than Campsite B?

   A 7 ft

   B 12 ft

   C 17 ft

   D 67 ft

6. Maurice shot 2 under par, or −2, on each of the first 4 holes of golf. What is his score with respect to par after the fourth hole?

   A 8   C −4

   B 4   D −8

7. The temperature dropped 12 degrees in 3 hours. What was the average change in temperature each hour?

   A −9°   C 4°

   B −4°   D 9°

Numeration, Patterns, and Relationships (continued)

Read each question. Then mark your answer on the sheet.

---

8. What are the coordinates of point *D*?

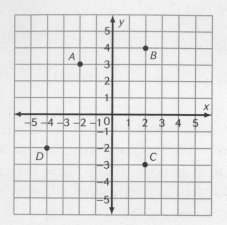

A (−4, −2)   C (2, 4)

B (2, −3)   D (−2, 3)

---

9. Write an expression to describe the relationship in the table.

m	0	5	6	8
n	−1	9	11	15

A $3m + 1$ C $\frac{m}{2} + 1$

B $2m − 1$ D $1 + 4m$

---

10. Carla earns $5 each time she rakes the leaves. Use the table to find the equation that represents this situation.

Rakes	*x*	1	2	3	4
Money	*y*	5	10	15	20

A $y = x + 4$ C $y = 5x$

B $y = x + 5$ D $y = x − 5$

---

11. Jamal drew the graph shown. Which equation did he use?

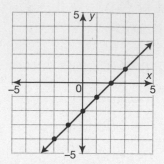

A $y = x − 2$

B $y = x + 2$

C $y = 2x$

D $y = x ÷ 2$

---

12. Which computation should you do first to evaluate this expression?

$$9 − 5 \times 1 + 18 ÷ 2 + 5$$

A $9 − 5$

B $1 + 18$

C $18 ÷ 2$

D 5×1

---

13. A pound is 16 ounces. Which expression shows the number of ounces in *p* pounds?

A $16p$

B $16 − p$

C $16 + p$

D $16 ÷ p$

104

Numeration, Patterns, and Relationships (continued)

Read each question. Then mark your answer on the sheet.

---

14. Name the property used in the equation.

$(7 \times 4) \times 12 = 7 \times (4 \times 12)$

A Distributive Property

B Associative Property

C Commutative Property

D Zero Property

---

15. Solve the equation
$10.8 = n - 2.4$.

A $n = 8.0$

B $n = 8.4$

C $n = 12.2$

D $n = 13.2$

---

16. You pay $63.43 for a video game. The amount includes a tax of $3.48. Which equation can be used to find c, the cost of the video game before tax?

A $c + 3.48 = 63.43$

B $c - 3.48 = 63.43$

C $c + 63.43 = 3.48$

D $c - 63.43 = 3.48$

---

17. Solve $x - \frac{3}{4} = 2\frac{3}{8}$.

A $x = 1\frac{5}{8}$

B $x = 3\frac{1}{8}$

C $x = 3\frac{1}{6}$

D $x = 3\frac{1}{2}$

---

18. Solve $16h = 2\frac{2}{3}$.

A $h = \frac{1}{6}$

B $h = 13\frac{1}{3}$

C $h = 18\frac{2}{3}$

D $h = 42\frac{2}{3}$

---

19. Solve $5t = -35$.

A $t = 245$

B $t = 7$

C $t = -7$

D $t = -245$

---

20. Solve $2x - 5 = 17$.

A $x = 6$

B $x = 11$

C $x = 24$

D $x = 44$

Operations with Whole Numbers

Read each question. Then mark your answer on the sheet.

---

21. Traci wants to find 3×498 mentally. Which of the following strategies should she use?

A $(3 \times 400) - (3 \times 90)$

B $(3 \times 400) + (3 \times 90)$

C $(3 \times 500) + (3 \times 2)$

D $(3 \times 500) - (3 \times 2)$

---

22. Which equals 2^7?

A 14

B 32

C 64

D 128

---

23. Which is the prime factorization of 48?

A $2^3 \times 3$

B $2^4 \times 3$

C 3×16

D 6×8

---

24. Which number is divisible by 3?

A 46   **C** 96

B 58   **D** 101

---

25. What is the GCF of 15 and 20?

A 3

B 4

C 5

D 9

---

26. Maria's parents do not have to work this Saturday. Her mom gets every sixth day off. Her dad gets every fourth day off. How long will it be until they both get a day off together again?

A 12 days

B 24 days

C 84 days

D 96 days

---

27. The art teacher has 36 small sticks and 60 pipe cleaners for art projects. He wants to make kits for the students using all the sticks and pipe cleaners. All the kits must be alike. He wants to make as many kits as possible. What is the greatest number of kits he can make?

A 8 kits

B 9 kits

C 12 kits

D 36 kits

Fractions, Decimals, and Percents

Read each question. Then mark your answer on the sheet.

---

28. Gina works in a shoe store. During a sale, she sold 42 pairs of shoes. Before the sale started, there were 84 pairs of shoes in stock. In simplest form, what fractional part of the stock did Gina sell?

A $\frac{3}{4}$

B $\frac{1}{2}$

C $\frac{1}{3}$

D $\frac{1}{6}$

---

29. Which of the following shows numbers in order from least to greatest?

A 3.1, 2.99, 2.9, 0.31

B 2.9, 2.99, 0.31, 3.1

C 0.31, 2.99, 2.9, 3.1

D 0.31, 2.9, 2.99, 3.1

---

30. Which number does not equal $\frac{22}{8}$?

A $2\frac{3}{4}$

B 2.25

C 2.75

D $2\frac{6}{8}$

---

31. Jamie's cat weighs $6\frac{1}{4}$ pounds. Her dog weighs $9\frac{7}{8}$ pounds. About how much more does Jamie's dog weigh than her cat?

A About 3 pounds

B About 4 pounds

C About 5 pounds

D About 6 pounds

---

32. $7\frac{1}{4}$
$-5\frac{3}{8}$

A $1\frac{7}{8}$

B $2\frac{1}{8}$

C $2\frac{1}{2}$

D $2\frac{7}{8}$

---

33. Kira gave handball lessons for $5\frac{3}{4}$ hours on Saturday and $3\frac{2}{3}$ hours on Sunday. How many hours did she teach in all?

A $10\frac{5}{12}$ hours

B $9\frac{5}{12}$ hours

C $8\frac{5}{12}$ hours

D $2\frac{1}{12}$ hours

Fractions, Decimals, and Percents (continued)

Read each question. Then mark your answer on the sheet.

---

34. How many one-eighths are in 2?

   A $\frac{1}{16}$ **C** 8

   B $\frac{2}{8}$ **D** 16

---

35. During a race Li averaged $10\frac{2}{5}$ miles per hour for $2\frac{3}{5}$ hours. Which is the best estimate of the total distance he ran?

   A 20 miles

   B 22 miles

   C 30 miles

   D 33 miles

---

36. What is $2\frac{5}{8} \times \frac{2}{7}$?

   A $\frac{1}{2}$

   B $\frac{3}{4}$

   C $1\frac{1}{7}$

   D $9\frac{3}{16}$

---

37. What is $3\frac{2}{3} \div \frac{5}{6}$?

   A $4\frac{2}{5}$

   B $3\frac{4}{5}$

   C $3\frac{1}{18}$

   D $2\frac{2}{3}$

---

38. $12.9 + 6.78 + 1.058 =$

   A 20.738

   B 21.738

   C 30.26

   D 91.28

---

39. $0.08 \times 0.09 =$

   A 0.72   **C** 0.0072

   B 0.072   **D** 0.00072

---

40. Mr. Littleton bought 67.5 pounds of hamburger. He wants to separate it into packages of 1.5 pounds. How many packages can he make?

   A 38 packages

   B 43 packages

   C 45 packages

   D 48 packages

---

41. Mr. Jones earns about 75,320 frequent flier miles per year. What is this number written in scientific notation?

   A 75.320×10^3

   B 7.532×10^3

   C 7.532×10^4

   D 0.7532×10^4

Fractions, Decimals, and Percents (continued)

Read each question. Then mark your answer on the sheet.

42. There are 6 squares, 9 rectangles, and 8 circles. What is the ratio of circles to rectangles?

A $\frac{6}{9}$ C $\frac{8}{9}$

B $\frac{8}{6}$ D $\frac{9}{6}$

43. Which store has the best buy on acrylic paint? What is its unit price?

Painter's Palette	
acrylic paint	2 for $7.50
brushes	2 for $5.25

The Hobby Shop	
acrylic paint	3 for $9.79
brushes	4 for $10.99

Art World	
acrylic paint	6 for $18.99
brushes	3 for $9.50

A The Hobby Shop; $3.27

B Art World; $3.75

C Art World; $3.17

D The Hobby Shop; $3.17

44. A recipe calls for 1.5 cups of flour and 0.75 cup of sugar. Which proportion can be used to find f, the amount of flour needed to make this recipe with 1.25 cups of sugar?

A $\frac{1.5}{0.75} = \frac{f}{1.25}$ C $\frac{f}{1.5} = \frac{0.75}{1.25}$

B $\frac{1.5}{0.75} = \frac{1.25}{f}$ D $\frac{1.5}{f} = \frac{1.25}{0.75}$

45. You are making a scale drawing of your bedroom using a scale of 1 inch = 1.5 feet. The actual width of your bedroom is 12 feet. What width should your bedroom be on the scale drawing?

A 6 in.   C 9 in.

B 8 in.   D 18 in.

46. The formula $d = rt$ gives the relationship among distance, d, rate of speed, r, and time, t. Use the formula to find how long it would take to travel 217 miles at 62 miles per hour.

A 2 hours   C 3 hours

B 2.5 hours   D 3.5 hours

47. Which is the best estimate of 9% of 249?

A 2.5   C 25

B 20   D 30

48. You buy a pair of jeans that normally cost $35.99 for 25% off. Sales tax is 4.5%. How much do you pay?

A $9.45

B $26.99

C $28.07

D $28.21

Measurement and Geometry

Read each question. Then mark your answer on the sheet.

Use the figure for Questions 49 and 50.

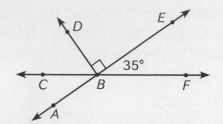

49. Which angle is complementary to ∠*DBC*?

A ∠*CBA*

B ∠*EBA*

C ∠*DBF*

D ∠*DBE*

50. What is the measure of ∠*CBE*?

A 35°

B 55°

C 145°

D 165°

51. How many edges does a pentagonal prism have?

A 15

B 12

C 10

D 5

52. Find the measure of ∠*P*.

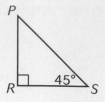

A 35°

B 45°

C 55°

D 125°

53. Which figure is a parallelogram with all 4 sides congruent?

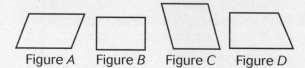

Figure *A*   Figure *B*   Figure *C*   Figure *D*

A Figure *A*

B Figure *B*

C Figure *C*

D Figure *D*

54. What type of transformation was used to move Figure I to Figure II?

Fig. I

Fig. II

A Translation

B Rotation

C Reflection

D Glide

110

Measurement and Geometry (continued)

Read each question. Then mark your answer on the sheet.

---

55. There are 30 quarts of milk on the grocery's shelves. How many gallons is this?

A 60 gallons

B 8 gallons

C 7.5 gallons

D 6 gallons

---

56. Find the missing number.

$$92 \text{ mL} = \blacksquare \text{ L}$$

A 0.092   **C** 920

B 0.92   **D** 92,000

---

57. About how many pounds is 9 kilograms?

$$1 \text{ kg} \approx 2.2 \text{ lb}$$

A 5 pounds

B 10 pounds

C 20 pounds

D 40 pounds

---

58. Subtract.   23 h 35 min
            − 15 h 17 min

A 8 h 18 min

B 8 h 52 min

C 38 h 18 min

D 38 h 52 min

---

59. Which measurement is most precise?

A 5 mm

B 5 cm

C 50 cm

D 0.5 m

---

60. The perimeter of a rectangular park is 840 yards. The park is 170 yards wide. If ℓ stands for the length of the park, which equation can be used to find ℓ?

A $840 - 2\ell = 170$

B $2\ell + 340 = 840$

C $\ell + 340 = 840$

D $170\ell = 840$

---

61. Find the area of the parallelogram.

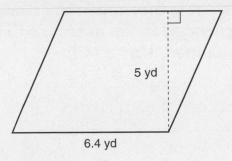

5 yd

6.4 yd

A 32 yd^2

B 30.2 yd^2

C 30 yd^2

D 22.8 yd^2

Measurement and Geometry (continued)

Read each question. Then mark your answer on the sheet.

---

62. **Find the area of the triangle.**

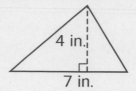

4 in.

7 in.

A 14 in.²

B 28 in.²

C 30 in.²

D 56 in.²

---

63. **A water sprinkler in the center
of a garden shoots water for a
distance of 4 m in all directions.
Caleb plans to put a small fence
around the area being watered.
How long should the fence be?
Use 3.14 for π.**

A 6.28 m   **C** 12.66 m

B 12.56 m   **D** 25.12 m

---

64. **What is the area of the circle,
rounded to the nearest whole
number? Use 3.14 for π.**

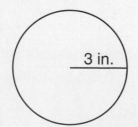

3 in.

A 9 in.²   **C** 28 in.²

B 19 in.²   **D** 113 in.²

---

65. **Find the volume of the prism.**

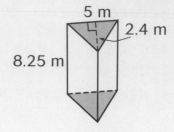

5 m

2.4 m

8.25 m

A 12 m³

B 48.5 m³

C 49.5 m³

D 99 m³

---

66. **Find the surface area of the
cylinder below. Use 3.14 for π.**

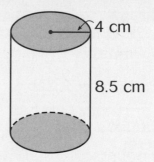

4 cm

8.5 cm

A About 427 cm²

B About 314 cm²

C About 72 cm²

D About 50 cm²

Data Analysis and Probability

Read each question. Then mark your answer on the sheet.

---

67. The histogram shows the ages of people who entered an amusement park the first hour of opening day.

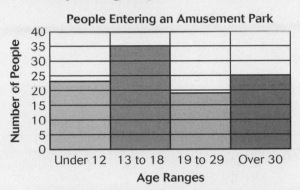

The frequency table below was used to make the histogram. What is the missing number in the table?

Age Range	Frequency
Under 12	23
13 to 18	?
19 to 29	19
Over 30	25

A 37   **C** 32

B 35   **D** 18

---

68. In a survey of 100 people, 25 said their favorite amusement park ride is the roller coaster. Susi is making a circle graph of the results. What fraction of the graph should she make the roller coaster sector?

A $\frac{1}{4}$ **C** $\frac{2}{5}$

B $\frac{1}{3}$ **D** $\frac{1}{2}$

---

69. Which is the most appropriate display for the favorite activities of children at summer camp?

A Bar graph

B Line graph

C Circle graph

D Stem-and-leaf plot

---

70. The stem-and-leaf diagram shows the number of school bus riders during May. Find the median of the data.

Stem	Leaf
1	0 2 5 5 8 8
2	1 3
3	0 2 6 8 9

A 1   **C** 21

B 18   **D** 22

---

71. The following represent amounts Thom earned babysitting.

$17 $20 $17 $33 $22 $23

What is Thom's mean income?

A $17

B $21

C $22

D $33

Data Analysis and Probability (continued)

Read each question. Then mark your answer on the sheet.

72. Each set of data below gives the heights of 4 trees, in feet. For which set of data does the median give a better indication of the typical height than the mean?

    A 12, 26, 35, 14

    B 15, 18, 11, 22

    C 19, 16, 43, 10

    D 36, 28, 19, 32

Use the following for Questions 73 and 74.

To learn what voters think about a tax to build a new gym, you send a questionnaire to parents of sixth-grade students.

73. What is the population being studied?

    A Sixth-grade students

    B Parents of sixth-grade students

    C People who use the gym

    D Voters in the school district

74. Which question is most fair?

    A Are you willing to pay extra taxes?

    B Will you vote for or against the tax for a new gym?

    C Do you want a new gym?

    D Will you vote for the tax?

75. Identify the sampling method: A person asks those entering a mall about their favorite beverage.

    A Random sampling

    B Responses to a survey

    C Convenience sampling

    D Systematic sampling

76. Which sample is likely to be unbiased?

    A Choosing random phone numbers to ask people their preferred cleaning product.

    B Having a candidate ask voters whom they plan to vote for.

    C Asking readers to return a survey about their income.

    D Asking the Spanish club their preferred eating establishment.

77. Mrs. Arnold is planning dinner. She has 4 choices of a main dish: chicken, meatloaf, hamburgers, and fish. She has 2 choices of vegetables: beans and peas. How many different meals could she prepare with one choice of each main dish and vegetable?

    A 6   C 12

    B 8   D 16

Data Analysis and Probability (continued)

Read each question. Then mark your answer on the sheet.

78. There are 6 class officers. How many ways can 2 of these students be selected to serve on a committee?

    A 60   C 15

    B 30   D 12

Use the spinner for Questions 79–81.

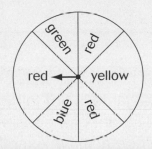

79. You spin the spinner once. Find *P*(not red).

    A $\frac{3}{8}$ C $\frac{5}{8}$

    B $\frac{1}{2}$ D $\frac{3}{4}$

80. You spin the spinner once. Find *P*(red).

    A 37.5%   C 62.5%

    B 50%   D 75%

81. You spin the spinner twice. Find *P*(red, red).

    A $\frac{1}{64}$ C $\frac{1}{4}$

    B $\frac{9}{64}$ D $\frac{3}{4}$

82. Suzanne got 12 hits in her first 18 times at bat. She expects to bat 3 times in today's game. How many hits should she get?

    A None

    B 1 hit

    C 2 hits

    D 3 hits

Use the following for Questions 83 and 84.

The letters of the word MIDDLE are placed in a bag. You draw two letters without looking.

83. What is the probability both letters drawn are D?

    A $\frac{1}{15}$

    B $\frac{1}{9}$

    C $\frac{8}{15}$

    D $\frac{2}{3}$

84. Which best describes the events of drawing two Ds from the bag?

    A Dependent events

    B Independent events

    C Mutually exclusive events

    D Complementary events

Problem Solving

Read each question. Then mark your answer on the sheet.

---

85. The fruit market has peaches for $1.49 per pound and apples for $1.29 per pound. What is the total cost of 4 pounds of peaches and 2 pounds of apples?

A $5.16

B $5.96

C $8.14

D $8.54

---

86. Movie tickets cost $5.00 for children and $8.00 for adults. On Thursday, the movie theater sold 110 tickets and collected $820. How many childrens' tickets were sold?

A 90 tickets

B 45 tickets

C 20 tickets

D 10 tickets

---

87. Al played a game and finished with 62 points. During the game he earned 300 points, lost 250 points, earned 15 points, lost 25 points, and lost 10 points. How many points did Al have at the beginning of the game?

A 16   C 32

B 30   D 178

---

88. Kira and Joe are playing a game. They toss 3 plastic chips which are red on one side and blue on the other side. If exactly 2 chips turn up red, Joe gets a point. Otherwise, Kira gets a point. Make a list of all possible outcomes and use it to explain why the game is or is not fair.

RRR
RRB
RBB

A The game is not fair because only 3 out of 8 possible outcomes have exactly 2 red.

B The game is not fair because only 1 out of 4 possible outcomes have exactly 2 red.

C The game is fair because 4 out of 8 possible outcomes have exactly 2 red.

D The game is fair because 2 out of 4 possible outcomes have exactly 2 red.

---

89. It is normal to leave a 15% to 20% tip in a restaurant. Which of the following is the only reasonable tip to leave on a $26.55 bill?

A $2.66   C $12.00

B $4.00   D $25.00

Numeration, Patterns, and Relationships

Read each question. Then mark your answer on the sheet.

1. What is $(6 \times 10^{10}) + (2 \times 10^{9})$ in standard form?

   A 62,000,000,000

   B 60,200,000,000

   C 6,200,000,000

   D 6,020,000,000

2. Which day was the coldest?

Day	Low Temperature
Monday	−5° C
Tuesday	−2° C
Wednesday	−8° C
Thursday	−12° C

   A Monday

   B Tuesday

   C Wednesday

   D Thursday

3. Of the numbers $-\frac{5}{7}$, 0.55, 0.7, and $\frac{3}{4}$, which is the farthest to right on the number line?

   A $-\frac{5}{7}$

   B 0.55

   C 0.7

   D $\frac{3}{4}$

4. What is $-5 + (-8)$?

   A −13   C 3

   B −3   D 13

5. The temperature at noon was −2°F. At 3:00 P.M. the temperature had dropped by 9°F. What was the temperature at 3:00 P.M.?

   A −11°F

   B −7°F

   C 7°F

   D 11°F

6. At noon, the temperature was 0°F. For the next 5 hours the temperature dropped by 4° each hour. What was the temperature at 5:00?

   A 20°F

   B 10°F

   C −10°F

   D −20°F

7. After 3 holes of golf, Lisa had a score of −6. What was her average score per hole?

   A −3   C 2

   B −2   D 3

117

Read each question. Then mark your answer on the sheet.

---

8. What are the coordinates of point *B*?

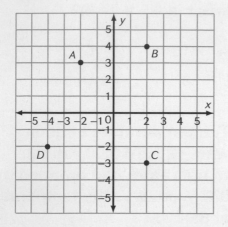

   A $(-4, -2)$ **C** $(2, 4)$

   B $(2, -3)$ **D** $(2-, 3)$

---

9. Write an expression to describe the relationship in the table.

m	8	4	2	0
n	5	3	2	1

   A $\frac{m}{4} + 1$ **C** $\frac{m}{2} + 1$

   B $2m - 1$ **D** $4m - 3$

---

10. It costs Tom $4 to rent a movie. Use the table to find the equation that represents the situation.

Money	*x*	4	8	12	16
Movies	*y*	1	2	3	4

   A $y = x \div 4$ **C** $y = x + 3$

   B $y = 4x$ **D** $y = x - 3$

---

11. Mary Beth drew the graph shown. Which equation did she use?

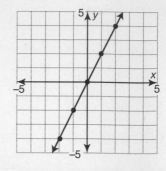

   A $y = x - 2$

   B $y = x + 2$

   C $y = 2x$

   D $y = x \div 2$

---

12. Which computation should you do first to evaluate this expression?

   $$10 - 8 \div 2 + 5 \times 4 + 7$$

   A $10 - 8$

   B $2 + 5$

   C $8 \div 2$

   D 5×4

---

13. A yard is 36 inches. Which expression shows the number of inches in *y* yards?

   A $36 \div y$

   B $36y$

   C $36 + y$

   D $36 - y$

Numeration, Patterns, and Relationships (continued)

Read each question. Then mark your answer on the sheet.

14. Name the property used in the equation.

$$314 \times 1 = 314$$

A Zero Property

B Distributive Property

C Associative Property

D Identity Property

15. Solve the equation $x + 4.5 = 7.8$.

A 1.23

B 3.3

C 12.3

D 35.1

16. Ryan can type 40 words per minute. Which equation can be used to find how many minutes, m, it would take him to type 1,000 words?

A $m + 40 = 1,000$

B $m - 40 = 1,000$

C $40m = 1,000$

D $m \div 40 = 1,000$

17. Solve $y - \frac{3}{5} = 2\frac{7}{10}$.

A $y = 2\frac{1}{10}$

B $y = 3\frac{3}{10}$

C $y = 3\frac{2}{3}$

D $y = 4\frac{1}{2}$

18. Solve $1\frac{3}{7}n = 1\frac{1}{4}$.

A $n = \frac{5}{28}$

B $n - \frac{7}{8}$

C $n = 2\frac{19}{28}$

D $n = 3\frac{4}{7}$

19. Solve $h + 17 = 9$.

A $h = 26$

B $h = 8$

C $h = -2$

D $h = -8$

20. Solve $2x - 7 = 13$.

A $x = 20$

B $x = 12$

C $x = 10$

D $x = 3$

Operations with Whole Numbers

Read each question. Then mark your answer on the sheet.

21. **Branden wants to find
$(4 \times 27) \times 25$ mentally. Which
of the following strategies
should he use?**

    A $(4 \times 20) + (4 \times 5)$

    B $(27 \times 20) + (27 \times 5)$

    C $27 \times (4 \times 25)$

    D $4 \times (27 \times 25)$

22. **Which equals 3^4?**

    A 81

    B 27

    C 12

    D 9

23. **Which is the prime factorization
of 180?**

    A $2 \times 3^2 \times 10$

    B 5×3^4

    C $2^2 \times 3^2 \times 5$

    D $2 \times 5 \times 18$

24. **Which number is not divisible
by 3?**

    A 51

    B 47

    C 39

    D 24

25. **What is the GCF of 16 and 20?**

    A 8

    B 4

    C 2

    D 1

26. **Sage travels around a go-
cart track every 3 minutes.
Marcus travels around it every
4 minutes, and Thomas travels
around it every 6 minutes. They
all start together. How long will
it be until they all three get back
to the start at the same time?**

    A 6 minutes

    B 12 minutes

    C 18 minutes

    D 24 minutes

27. **Louise is making bags of party
favors. She has 16 stickers and
24 candies. She wants each
bag to be alike, and she needs
to use all of the stickers and
candies. What is the greatest
number of party bags she can
make?**

    A 2 bags

    B 4 bags

    C 8 bags

    D 16 bags

Fractions, Decimals, and Percents

Read each question. Then mark your answer on the sheet.

28. James plays basketball. During practice, he made 18 baskets. He shot 24 times. In simplest form, what fractional part of the times he shot did James make a basket?

    A $\frac{3}{4}$

    B $\frac{2}{3}$

    C $\frac{1}{2}$

    D $\frac{3}{8}$

29. Which of the following shows numbers in order from least to greatest?

    A 0.52, 4.8, 4.88, 5.2

    B 0.52, 4.88, 4.8, 5.2

    C 4.88, 4.8, 0.52, 5.2

    D 5.2, 4.88, 4.8, 0.52

30. Which number does not equal $\frac{26}{8}$?

    A 3.75

    B 3.25

    C $3\frac{1}{4}$

    D $3\frac{2}{8}$

31. Hanna has $4\frac{4}{5}$ pounds of apples. Megan has $2\frac{9}{10}$ pounds of apples. About how many more pounds of apples does Hanna have than Megan?

    A About 2 pounds

    B About 3 pounds

    C About 7 pounds

    D About 9 pounds

32. $5\frac{1}{3}$
    $-2\frac{4}{9}$

    A $3\frac{8}{9}$

    D $3\frac{1}{3}$

    C $3\frac{1}{9}$

    D $2\frac{8}{9}$

33. Gina needs $3\frac{5}{6}$ cups of milk for one recipe and $1\frac{1}{4}$ cups of milk for another. How much milk does she need in all?

    A $4\frac{3}{4}$ cups

    B $4\frac{5}{6}$ cups

    C $4\frac{11}{12}$ cups

    D $5\frac{1}{12}$ cups

Fractions, Decimals, and Percents (continued)

Read each question. Then mark your answer on the sheet.

---

34. How many one-fourths are in 4?

A $\frac{1}{4}$ 　　　　C 16

B $\frac{2}{4}$ 　　　　D 44

---

35. Rachael's plant is growing an average of $3\frac{3}{4}$ inches a week. This month has $4\frac{2}{7}$ weeks. Which is the best estimate of the total amount the plant will grow this month?

A 16 in.

B 12 in.

C 9 in.

D 6 in.

---

36. What is $3\frac{3}{5} \times \frac{4}{9}$?

A $1\frac{1}{9}$

B $1\frac{1}{2}$

C $1\frac{3}{5}$

D $8\frac{1}{10}$

---

37. What is $4\frac{1}{2} \div \frac{3}{4}$?

A 12

B 6

C $4\frac{1}{2}$

D $3\frac{3}{8}$

---

38. $18.3 - 7.952 =$

A 10.348

B 10.352

C 10.452

D 11.652

---

39. $0.05 \times 0.04 =$

A 0.0002 　　　C 0.020

B 0.002 　　　　D 0.02

---

40. Tanisha had a piece of yarn 76.5 inches long. She cut it into pieces that were each 4.5 inches long. How many pieces did she cut?

A 7 pieces

B 16 pieces

C 17 pieces

D 18 pieces

---

41. Earth is about 93 million miles from the Sun. What is this number written in scientific notation?

A 9.3×10^6

B 9.3×10^7

C 9.3×10^8

D 9.3×10^9

122

Fractions, Decimals, and Percents (continued)

Read each question. Then mark your answer on the sheet.

42. Forrest sorts some shapes by color. There are 11 red, 9 blue, and 3 purple. What is the ratio of purple shapes to red shapes?

A $\frac{3}{11}$ C $\frac{11}{3}$

B $\frac{9}{11}$ D $\frac{11}{9}$

43. Which store has the best buy on brushes? What is its unit price?

Painter's Palette	
acrylic paint	2 for $7.50
brushes	2 for $5.25

The Hobby Shop	
acrylic paint	3 for $9.79
brushes	4 for $10.99

Art World	
acrylic paint	6 for $18.99
brushes	3 for $9.50

A Painter's Palette; $2.63

B The Hobby Shop; $2.75

C Painter's Palette; $2.25

D Art World; $3.17

44. A photograph that measures 5 in. wide by 7 in. high is reduced to fit into a space that is 1.4 in. high. Which proportion can be used to find w, the width of the reduced photo?

A $\frac{5}{7} = \frac{w}{1.4}$ C $\frac{w}{5} = \frac{7}{1.4}$

B $\frac{5}{7} = \frac{1.4}{w}$ D $\frac{5}{1.4} = \frac{7}{w}$

45. A map has a scale of 2 cm = 5 km. The distance between two cities on the map is 31.2 cm. What is the actual distance between the cities?

A 12.48 km

B 62.4 km

C 78 km

D 156 km

46. The formula $d = rt$ gives the relationship among distance, d, rate of speed, r, and time, t. Use the formula to find how fast you need to drive to travel 252 miles in 4.5 hours.

A 54 mph   C 58 mph

B 56 mph   D 60 mph

47. Which is the best estimate of 52% of 248?

A 100   C 150

B 124   D 200

48. You buy a CD that normally costs $16.99 for 20% off. Sales tax is 5.5%. How much do you pay?

A $13.59

B $14.27

C $14.34

D $14.41

Measurement and Geometry

Read each question. Then mark your answer on the sheet.

Use this figure for Questions 49 and 50.

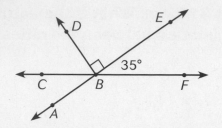

49. Which angle is supplementary to ∠ABC?

A ∠CBE

B ∠CBF

C ∠CBD

D ∠FBE

50. What is the measure of ∠ABD?

A 55°

B 70°

C 90°

D 145°

51. How many edges does a pentagonal pyramid have?

A 5

B 10

C 12

D 15

52. Find the measure of ∠J.

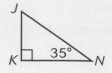

A 35°

B 55°

C 65°

D 135°

---

53. Which figure is a parallelogram with 4 right angles?

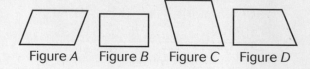

Figure A   Figure B   Figure C   Figure D

A Figure A

B Figure B

C Figure C

D Figure D

---

54. What type of transformation was used to move Figure I to Figure II?

Fig. I   Fig. II

A Translation

B Rotation

C Reflection

D Glide

Measurement and Geometry (continued)

Read each question. Then mark your answer on the sheet.

55. Mark bought $3\frac{1}{2}$ gallons of water. How many quarts is this?

    A 14 qt

    B 12 qt

    C 6 qt

    D 0.75 qt

56. Find the missing number.

    $$8.4 \text{ kg} = \blacksquare \text{ g}$$

    A 0.84

    B 84

    C 840

    D 8,400

57. About how many centimeters is 8 inches?

    $$1 \text{ in.} = 2.54 \text{ cm}$$

    A 4 cm

    B 16 cm

    C 18 cm

    D 20 cm

58. Add.   30 h 28 min
         $\underline{+ \text{ 17 h 31 min}}$

    A 12 h 57 min

    B 47 h 59 min

    C 48 h 9 min

    D 49 h 49 min

59. Which measurement is most precise?

    A 800 mm

    B 8 cm

    C 80 cm

    D 0.8 m

60. One side of a rectangular banner is 14 inches long. The perimeter is 48 inches. If ℓ stands for the length of the banner, which equation can be used to find ℓ?

    A $48 - 2\ell - 14$

    B $14\ell = 48$

    C $\ell + 28 = 48$

    D $2\ell + 28 - 48$

61. A design contains parallelograms that are 8 cm long and 6.2 cm high. What is the area of each parallelogram?

    A 49.6 cm^2

    B 48.6 cm^2

    C 28.4 cm^2

    D 14.2 cm^2

Measurement and Geometry (continued)

Read each question. Then mark your answer on the sheet.

62. **Find the area of the triangle.**

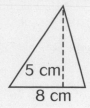

5 cm
8 cm

A 20 cm²

B 30 cm²

C 40 cm²

D 80 cm²

63. **Shaundra is making a cylindrical wastebasket for her room. She plans to decorate it by gluing strips of braid around it. If the diameter of the wastebasket is 12 inches, how long should each strip of braid be, to the nearest inch? Use 3.14 for π.**

A 6 in.   **C** 38 in.

B 36 in.   **D** 75 in.

64. **What is the area of the circle, rounded to the nearest whole number? Use 3.14 for π.**

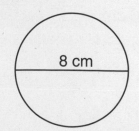

8 cm

A 25 cm²   **C** 100 cm²

B 50 cm²   **D** 200 cm²

65. **Find the volume of the prism.**

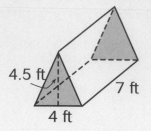

4.5 ft   7 ft
4 ft

A 126 ft³

B 63 ft³

C 62.5 ft³

D 18 ft³

66. **Find the surface area of the cylinder. Use 3.14 for π.**

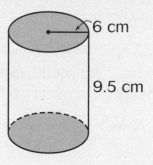

6 cm

9.5 cm

A About 358 cm²

B About 471 cm²

C About 1,584 cm²

D About 1,074 cm²

Data Analysis and Probability

Read each question. Then mark your answer on the sheet.

---

67. The histogram shows the ages of people who entered a museum the first hour of opening day.

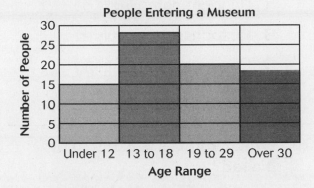

People Entering a Museum

The frequency table below, was used to make the histogram. What is the missing number in the table?

Age Range	Frequency
Under 12	15
13 to 18	28
19 to 29	?
Over 30	18

A 28   **C** 19

B 20   **D** 15

---

68. In a survey of 90 people, 30 said their favorite artist is Monet. Marco is making a circle graph of the results. What fraction of the graph should he make the Monet sector?

A $\frac{1}{4}$ **C** $\frac{2}{5}$

B $\frac{1}{3}$ **D** $\frac{1}{2}$

---

69. Which is the most appropriate display for the favorite type of lunch sandwich of children?

A Line graph

B Circle graph

C Bar graph

D Stem-and-leaf plot

---

70. The stem-and-leaf diagram shows test scores. Find the median of the data.

Stem	Leaf
6	0 1 1 2 4
7	0 0 3 3 8 9
8	2 2 2 2 3 3 3 5

A 8   **C** 75.5

B 73   **D** 78

---

71. The following represents the sizes of bicycle tires of several recreational bikes.

18 inches, 24 inches, 24 inches, and 26 inches

What is the mean bicycle tire size?

A 18 in.

B 22 in.

C 23 in.

D 24 in.

Data Analysis and Probability (continued)

Read each question. Then mark your answer on the sheet.

72. Each set of data below gives the amount of snow, in inches, for four days. For which set of data does the median give a better indication of the typical amount of snow over those days than the mean?

    A 2, 1, 21, 6   **C** 6, 8, 3, 7

    B 12, 15, 8, 5   **D** 3, 5, 2, 4

Use the following for Questions 73 and 74.

You want to know what students think about saving a park. You give a questionnaire to all sixth graders in your school.

73. What is the population being studied?

    A All students in the state

    B Sixth-graders in your school

    C Everyone in your school

    D All students around the park

74. Which question is most fair?

    A Do you want the trees cut down?

    B Do you think a mall is important?

    C Are you against a mini-mall?

    D Are you for or against replacing Center Park with a mall?

75. Identify the sampling method: The principal chooses every 5th student from an alphabetical list to ask about lunch preferences.

    A Random sampling

    B Responses to a survey

    C Convenience sampling

    D Systematic sampling

76. Which sample is likely to be biased?

    A Calling every 5th number in a phone book and asking about the upcoming election in a town.

    B Asking the girl students to return a survey about their favorite books.

    C Asking each member of the Math Club about his or her preference for an end of the year club party.

    D Pulling every 3rd registration sheet to find the mean number of siblings of students in the school.

Data Analysis and Probability (continued)

Read each question. Then mark your answer on the sheet.

77. Flyaway Airlines provides lunches for its passengers. Lunches consist of a choice of banana or apple; roast beef, turkey, peanut butter, or pita sandwich; and cookie, yogurt, or cake. If each lunch consists of a piece of fruit, a sandwich, and a dessert, how many different lunches can the airline provide?

    A 8   C 24

    B 9   D 32

78. How many ways can you choose 3 flowers from 7?

    A 21   C 35

    B 24   D 210

Use the spinner for Questions 79–81.

79. You spin the spinner once. Find P(not 6).

    A $\frac{1}{8}$ C $\frac{3}{4}$

    B $\frac{1}{4}$ D $\frac{7}{8}$

80. You spin the spinner once. Find P(less than 3).

    A 25%   C 50%

    B 37.5%   D 62.5%

81. You spin the spinner twice. Find P(more than 6, less than 4).

    A $\frac{1}{32}$ C $\frac{3}{8}$

    B $\frac{3}{32}$ D $\frac{5}{8}$

82. Maurice made 6 baskets in 15 shots during the last game. If he shoots only 10 times in today's game, how many baskets should he get?

    A 3 baskets   C 5 baskets

    B 4 baskets   D 8 baskets

Use the following for Questions 83 and 84.

The letters of the word SCHOOLS are placed in a bag. You draw two letters without looking.

83. What is the probability both letters drawn are S?

    A $\frac{1}{21}$ C $\frac{2}{7}$

    B $\frac{1}{6}$ D $\frac{19}{42}$

84. Which best describes the events of drawing two Ss from the bag?

    A Dependent events

    B Independent events

    C Mutually exclusive events

    D Complementary events

Problem Solving

Read each question. Then mark your answer on the sheet.

---

85. Bolts sell for $1.29 per pound and nails for $3.29 per pound. Find the total cost of 5 pounds of bolts and 3 pounds of nails?

   A $9.87

   B $16.32

   C $16.45

   D $20.32

---

86. A book of ride tickets cost $5.00 and a book of game tickets cost $3.00. The carnival sold 105 books of tickets and collected $351. How many books of ride tickets were sold?

   A 90

   B 87

   C 36

   D 18

---

87. A store owner reduced the price of a television by $50. Then he cut the price in half. The final sale price was $120. What was the original price?

   A $10

   B $110

   C $190

   D $290

---

88. Pablo and Suzie are playing a game. They spin 3 spinners which are each half green and half yellow. If exactly 2 spinners land on green, Suzie gets a point. Otherwise, Pablo gets a point. Make a list of all possible outcomes and use it to explain why the game is or is not fair.

GGG
GGY
GYY

   A The game is not fair because only 3 out of 8 possible outcomes have exactly 2 green.

   B The game is not fair because only 1 out of 4 possible outcomes have exactly 2 green.

   C The game is fair because 4 out of 8 possible outcomes have exactly 2 green.

   D The game is fair because 2 out of 4 possible outcomes have exactly 2 green.

---

89. Sales tax is usually between 2% and 10%. Which of the following is the only reasonable tax on a $38.45 purchase?

   A $7.69   **C** $2.31

   B $4.61   **D** $0.23

Answer Sheet

Mark the space that corresponds to the correct answer.   Form A ___ Forn

**Numeration, Patterns, and
Relationships**

1. Ⓐ   Ⓑ   Ⓒ   Ⓓ

2. Ⓐ   Ⓑ   Ⓒ   Ⓓ

3. Ⓐ   Ⓑ   Ⓒ   Ⓓ

4. Ⓐ   Ⓑ   Ⓒ   Ⓓ

5. Ⓐ   Ⓑ   Ⓒ   Ⓓ

6. Ⓐ   Ⓑ   Ⓒ   Ⓓ

7. Ⓐ   Ⓑ   Ⓒ   Ⓓ

8. Ⓐ   Ⓑ   Ⓒ   Ⓓ

9. Ⓐ   Ⓑ   Ⓒ   Ⓓ

10. Ⓐ   Ⓑ   Ⓒ   Ⓓ

11. Ⓐ   Ⓑ   Ⓒ   Ⓓ

12. Ⓐ   Ⓑ   Ⓒ   Ⓓ

13. Ⓐ   Ⓑ   Ⓒ   Ⓓ

14. Ⓐ   Ⓑ   Ⓒ   Ⓓ

15. Ⓐ   Ⓑ   Ⓒ   Ⓓ

16. Ⓐ   Ⓑ   Ⓒ   Ⓓ

17. Ⓐ   Ⓑ   Ⓒ   Ⓓ

18. Ⓐ   Ⓑ   Ⓒ   Ⓓ

19. Ⓐ   Ⓑ   Ⓒ   Ⓓ

20. Ⓐ   Ⓑ   Ⓒ   Ⓓ

Operations with Whole Numbers

21. Ⓐ   Ⓑ   Ⓒ   Ⓓ

22. Ⓐ   Ⓑ   Ⓒ   Ⓓ

23. Ⓐ   Ⓑ   Ⓒ   Ⓓ

24. Ⓐ   Ⓑ   Ⓒ   Ⓓ

25. Ⓐ   Ⓑ   Ⓒ   Ⓓ

26. Ⓐ   Ⓑ   Ⓒ   Ⓓ

27. Ⓐ   Ⓑ   Ⓒ   Ⓓ

Fractions, Decimals, and Percents

28. Ⓐ   Ⓑ   Ⓒ   Ⓓ

29. Ⓐ   Ⓑ   Ⓒ   Ⓓ

30. Ⓐ   Ⓑ   Ⓒ   Ⓓ

31. Ⓐ   Ⓑ   Ⓒ   Ⓓ

32. Ⓐ   Ⓑ   Ⓒ   Ⓓ

33. Ⓐ   Ⓑ   Ⓒ   Ⓓ

34. Ⓐ   Ⓑ   Ⓒ   Ⓓ

35. Ⓐ   Ⓑ   Ⓒ   Ⓓ

36. Ⓐ   Ⓑ   Ⓒ   Ⓓ

37. Ⓐ   Ⓑ   Ⓒ   Ⓓ

38. Ⓐ   Ⓑ   Ⓒ   Ⓓ

39. Ⓐ   Ⓑ   Ⓒ   Ⓓ

40. Ⓐ   Ⓑ   Ⓒ   Ⓓ

41. Ⓐ   Ⓑ   Ⓒ   Ⓓ

42. Ⓐ   Ⓑ   Ⓒ   Ⓓ

43. Ⓐ   Ⓑ   Ⓒ   Ⓓ

44. Ⓐ   Ⓑ   Ⓒ   Ⓓ

45. Ⓐ   Ⓑ   Ⓒ   Ⓓ

46. Ⓐ   Ⓑ   Ⓒ   Ⓓ

47. Ⓐ   Ⓑ   Ⓒ   Ⓓ

48. Ⓐ   Ⓑ   Ⓒ   Ⓓ

Answer Sheet (continued)

Mark the space that corresponds to the correct answer.   Form A ___ Form B ___

Measurement and Geometry

49. Ⓐ   Ⓑ   Ⓒ   Ⓓ
50. Ⓐ   Ⓑ   Ⓒ   Ⓓ
51. Ⓐ   Ⓑ   Ⓒ   Ⓓ
52. Ⓐ   Ⓑ   Ⓒ   Ⓓ
53. Ⓐ   Ⓑ   Ⓒ   Ⓓ
54. Ⓐ   Ⓑ   Ⓒ   Ⓓ
55. Ⓐ   Ⓑ   Ⓒ   Ⓓ
56. Ⓐ   Ⓑ   Ⓒ   Ⓓ
57. Ⓐ   Ⓑ   Ⓒ   Ⓓ
58. Ⓐ   Ⓑ   Ⓒ   Ⓓ
59. Ⓐ   Ⓑ   Ⓒ   Ⓓ
60. Ⓐ   Ⓑ   Ⓒ   Ⓓ
61. Ⓐ   Ⓑ   Ⓒ   Ⓓ
62. Ⓐ   Ⓑ   Ⓒ   Ⓓ
63. Ⓐ   Ⓑ   Ⓒ   Ⓓ
64. Ⓐ   Ⓑ   Ⓒ   Ⓓ
65. Ⓐ   Ⓑ   Ⓒ   Ⓓ
66. Ⓐ   Ⓑ   Ⓒ   Ⓓ

Data Analysis and Probability

67. Ⓐ   Ⓑ   Ⓒ   Ⓓ
68. Ⓐ   Ⓑ   Ⓒ   Ⓓ

69. Ⓐ   Ⓑ   Ⓒ   Ⓓ
70. Ⓐ   Ⓑ   Ⓒ   Ⓓ
71. Ⓐ   Ⓑ   Ⓒ   Ⓓ
72. Ⓐ   Ⓑ   Ⓒ   Ⓓ
73. Ⓐ   Ⓑ   Ⓒ   Ⓓ
74. Ⓐ   Ⓑ   Ⓒ   Ⓓ
75. Ⓐ   Ⓑ   Ⓒ   Ⓓ
76. Ⓐ   Ⓑ   Ⓒ   Ⓓ
77. Ⓐ   Ⓑ   Ⓒ   Ⓓ
78. Ⓐ   Ⓑ   Ⓒ   Ⓓ
79. Ⓐ   Ⓑ   Ⓒ   Ⓓ
80. Ⓐ   Ⓑ   Ⓒ   Ⓓ
81. Ⓐ   Ⓑ   Ⓒ   Ⓓ
82. Ⓐ   Ⓑ   Ⓒ   Ⓓ
83. Ⓐ   Ⓑ   Ⓒ   Ⓓ
84. Ⓐ   Ⓑ   Ⓒ   Ⓓ

Problem Solving

85. Ⓐ   Ⓑ   Ⓒ   Ⓓ
86. Ⓐ   Ⓑ   Ⓒ   Ⓓ
87. Ⓐ   Ⓑ   Ⓒ   Ⓓ
88. Ⓐ   Ⓑ   Ⓒ   Ⓓ
89. Ⓐ   Ⓑ   Ⓒ   Ⓓ

Name _____

Answer Key

Mark the space that corresponds to the correct answer.   Form A ✔   Form B ___

Numeration, Patterns, and Relationships

1. Ⓐ **Ⓑ** Ⓒ Ⓓ
2. **Ⓐ** Ⓑ Ⓒ Ⓓ
3. Ⓐ **Ⓑ** Ⓒ Ⓓ
4. **Ⓐ** Ⓑ Ⓒ Ⓓ
5. Ⓐ Ⓑ **Ⓒ** Ⓓ
6. Ⓐ Ⓑ Ⓒ **Ⓓ**
7. Ⓐ **Ⓑ** Ⓒ Ⓓ
8. **Ⓐ** Ⓑ Ⓒ Ⓓ
9. Ⓐ **Ⓑ** Ⓒ Ⓓ
10. Ⓐ Ⓑ **Ⓒ** Ⓓ
11. **Ⓐ** Ⓑ Ⓒ Ⓓ
12. Ⓐ Ⓑ Ⓒ **Ⓓ**
13. **Ⓐ** Ⓑ Ⓒ Ⓓ
14. Ⓐ **Ⓑ** Ⓒ Ⓓ
15. Ⓐ Ⓑ Ⓒ **Ⓓ**
16. **Ⓐ** Ⓑ Ⓒ Ⓓ
17. Ⓐ **Ⓑ** Ⓒ Ⓓ
18. **Ⓐ** Ⓑ Ⓒ Ⓓ
19. Ⓐ Ⓑ **Ⓒ** Ⓓ
20. Ⓐ **Ⓑ** Ⓒ Ⓓ

Operations with Whole Numbers

21. Ⓐ Ⓑ Ⓒ **Ⓓ**
22. Ⓐ Ⓑ Ⓒ **Ⓓ**
23. Ⓐ **Ⓑ** Ⓒ Ⓓ
24. Ⓐ Ⓑ **Ⓒ** Ⓓ
25. Ⓐ Ⓑ **Ⓒ** Ⓓ
26. **Ⓐ** Ⓑ Ⓒ Ⓓ
27. Ⓐ Ⓑ **Ⓒ** Ⓓ

Fractions, Decimals, and Percents

28. Ⓐ **Ⓑ** Ⓒ Ⓓ
29. Ⓐ Ⓑ Ⓒ **Ⓓ**
30. Ⓐ **Ⓑ** Ⓒ Ⓓ
31. Ⓐ **Ⓑ** Ⓒ Ⓓ
32. **Ⓐ** Ⓑ Ⓒ Ⓓ
33. Ⓐ **Ⓑ** Ⓒ Ⓓ
34. Ⓐ Ⓑ Ⓒ **Ⓓ**
35. Ⓐ Ⓑ **Ⓒ** Ⓓ
36. Ⓐ **Ⓑ** Ⓒ Ⓓ
37. **Ⓐ** Ⓑ Ⓒ Ⓓ
38. **Ⓐ** Ⓑ Ⓒ Ⓓ
39. Ⓐ Ⓑ **Ⓒ** Ⓓ
40. Ⓐ Ⓑ **Ⓒ** Ⓓ
41. Ⓐ Ⓑ **Ⓒ** Ⓓ
42. Ⓐ Ⓑ **Ⓒ** Ⓓ
43. Ⓐ Ⓑ **Ⓒ** Ⓓ
44. **Ⓐ** Ⓑ Ⓒ Ⓓ
45. Ⓐ **Ⓑ** Ⓒ Ⓓ
46. Ⓐ Ⓑ Ⓒ **Ⓓ**
47. Ⓐ Ⓑ **Ⓒ** Ⓓ
48. Ⓐ Ⓑ Ⓒ **Ⓓ**

Answer Key (continued)

Mark the space that corresponds to the correct answer.   Form A ✓   Form B ___

Measurement and Geometry

49. (A)● (B) (C) (D)
50. (A) (B) (C)● (D)
51. (A)● (B) (C) (D)
52. (A) (B)● (C) (D)
53. (A) (B) (C)● (D)
54. (A) (B)● (C) (D)
55. (A) (B) (C)● (D)
56. (A)● (B) (C) (D)
57. (A) (B) (C)● (D)
58. (A)● (B) (C) (D)
59. (A)● (B) (C) (D)
60. (A) (B)● (C) (D)
61. (A)● (B) (C) (D)
62. (A)● (B) (C) (D)
63. (A) (B) (C) (D)●
64. (A) (B) (C)● (D)
65. (A) (B) (C)● (D)
66. (A) (B)● (C) (D)

Data Analysis and Probability

67. (A) (B)● (C) (D)
68. (A)● (B) (C) (D)

69. (A) (B) (C)● (D)
70. (A) (B) (C)● (D)
71. (A) (B) (C)● (D)
72. (A) (B) (C)● (D)
73. (A) (B)● (C) (D)
74. (A) (B)● (C) (D)
75. (A) (B) (C)● (D)
76. (A)● (B) (C) (D)
77. (A) (B)● (C) (D)
78. (A) (B) (C)● (D)
79. (A) (B)● (C) (D)
80. (A) (B)● (C) (D)
81. (A) (B) (C)● (D)
82. (A) (B) (C)● (D)
83. (A)● (B) (C) (D)
84. (A)● (B) (C) (D)

Problem Solving

85. (A) (B) (C) (D)●
86. (A) (B) (C)● (D)
87. (A) (B) (C)● (D)
88. (A)● (B) (C) (D)
89. (A)● (B)● (C) (D)

Answer Key

Mark the space that corresponds to the correct answer.   Form A ___ Form B ✓

Numeration, Patterns, and Relationships

1. (Ⓐ) Ⓑ Ⓒ Ⓓ
2. Ⓐ Ⓑ Ⓒ (Ⓓ)
3. Ⓐ Ⓑ Ⓒ (Ⓓ)
4. (Ⓐ) Ⓑ Ⓒ Ⓓ
5. (Ⓐ) Ⓑ Ⓒ Ⓓ
6. Ⓐ Ⓑ Ⓒ (Ⓓ)
7. Ⓐ (Ⓑ) Ⓒ Ⓓ
8. Ⓐ Ⓑ (Ⓒ) Ⓓ
9. Ⓐ Ⓑ (Ⓒ) Ⓓ
10. (Ⓐ) Ⓑ Ⓒ Ⓓ
11. Ⓐ Ⓑ (Ⓒ) Ⓓ
12. Ⓐ Ⓑ (Ⓒ) Ⓓ
13. Ⓐ (Ⓑ) Ⓒ Ⓓ
14. Ⓐ Ⓑ Ⓒ (Ⓓ)
15. Ⓐ (Ⓑ) Ⓒ Ⓓ
16. Ⓐ Ⓑ (Ⓒ) Ⓓ
17. Ⓐ (Ⓑ) Ⓒ Ⓓ
18. Ⓐ (Ⓑ) Ⓒ Ⓓ
19. Ⓐ Ⓑ Ⓒ (Ⓓ)
20. (Ⓐ) Ⓑ (Ⓒ) Ⓓ

Operations with Whole Numbers

21. Ⓐ Ⓑ (Ⓒ) Ⓓ
22. (Ⓐ) Ⓑ Ⓒ Ⓓ
23. Ⓐ Ⓑ (Ⓒ) Ⓓ

24. Ⓐ (Ⓑ) Ⓒ Ⓓ
25. Ⓐ (Ⓑ) Ⓒ Ⓓ
26. Ⓐ (Ⓑ) Ⓒ Ⓓ
27. Ⓐ Ⓑ (Ⓒ) Ⓓ

Fractions, Decimals, and Percents

28. (Ⓐ) Ⓑ Ⓒ Ⓓ
29. (Ⓐ) Ⓑ Ⓒ Ⓓ
30. (Ⓐ) Ⓑ Ⓒ Ⓓ
31. (Ⓐ) Ⓑ Ⓒ Ⓓ
32. (Ⓐ) Ⓑ Ⓒ (Ⓓ)
33. Ⓐ Ⓑ Ⓒ (Ⓓ)
34. Ⓐ Ⓑ (Ⓒ) Ⓓ
35. (Ⓐ) Ⓑ Ⓒ Ⓓ
36. (Ⓐ) Ⓑ (Ⓒ) Ⓓ
37. Ⓐ (Ⓑ) Ⓒ Ⓓ
38. (Ⓐ) Ⓑ Ⓒ Ⓓ
39. Ⓐ (Ⓑ) Ⓒ Ⓓ
40. Ⓐ Ⓑ (Ⓒ) Ⓓ
41. Ⓐ (Ⓑ) Ⓒ Ⓓ
42. (Ⓐ) Ⓑ Ⓒ Ⓓ
43. (Ⓐ) Ⓑ Ⓒ Ⓓ
44. (Ⓐ) Ⓑ Ⓒ Ⓓ
45. (Ⓐ) Ⓑ (Ⓒ) Ⓓ
46. Ⓐ (Ⓑ) Ⓒ Ⓓ
47. Ⓐ (Ⓑ) Ⓒ Ⓓ
48. Ⓐ Ⓑ (Ⓒ) Ⓓ

Name _____

Answer Key (continued)

Mark the space that corresponds to the correct answer.   Form A ___   Form B ✓

Measurement and Geometry

49. (A) B C D
50. A B (C) D
51. A (B) C D
52. A (B) C D
53. A (B) C D
54. A B (C) D
55. (A) B C D
56. A B C (D)
57. A B C (D)
58. A (B) C D
59. A (B) C D
60. A B C (D)
61. (A) B C D
62. (A) B C D
63. A B (C) D
64. A (B) C D
65. A (B) C D
66. A B (C) D

Data Analysis and Probability

67. A (B) C D
68. A (B) C D

69. A (B) C D
70. A B C (D)
71. A B (C) D
72. (A) B C D
73. A (B) C D
74. A B C (D)
75. A B C (D)
76. A (B) C D
77. A B (C) D
78. A B C (D)
79. A B C (D)
80. (A) B C D
81. A (B) C D
82. A (B) C D
83. (A) B C D
84. (A) B C D

Problem Solving

85. A (B) C D
86. A B C (D)
87. A B C (D)
88. (A) B C D
89. A B (C) D